A Practical Approach to Caring

Kate Williams

(with contributions by Julie Hall)

PITMAN
PUBLISHING

PITMAN PUBLISHING
128 Long Acre, London, WC2E 9AN

A Division of Longman Group UK Limited

© Kate Williams 1991

First published in Great Britain 1991
Reprinted 1992, 1993

British Library Cataloguing in Publication Data

Williams, Kate
    Practical approach to caring.
    I. Title
    362.941

ISBN 0 273 03324-7

Printed in England by Clays Ltd, St Ives plc

Contents

Introduction

How to use this book

The 1990s will see the greatest changes in the delivery of care and health care since the Welfare State was established. The twin pillars of these changes, the government initiatives 'Working for Patients' in the NHS and 'Caring for People' in care in the community, provide the context for equally profound changes in staff training and accreditation. Beyond the headlines, however, the person who needs care, and the person offering care in this seamless network, must find a way forward. The carer must bring to the job not only specific skills but also kindness and understanding.

This book is designed as a core text for tutors and students involved in this process, in initial training or in-service. The book is relevant to a wide range of pre-professional training courses and training programmes in caring. Many assignments have been written specifically to meet the needs of students of all ages taking NVQ Levels 1 and 2 training validated by bodies such as BTEC and City and Guilds. Most assignments, and all the Case Studies, extend beyond this and offer material suitable to students taking NVQ Level 3, corresponding to BTEC National and NNEB. The book offers flexibility to the tutor in adapting the material to the needs of both full and part time students.

Part 1: Who Cares? provides an up-to-date outline of the new legislation and structures of the NHS and the local authority and an insight into what brought about these changes. The reader is invited to join in the debate and to look for solutions to the problems presented. Key points emerge from the reader's own analysis of data, interpretation of views and comprehension of material presented.

Part 2: Case Studies. These case histories invite the reader to respond to the needs, problems and individuality of a client, and, in the Activities that follow, to adopt a problem-solving approach to the dilemmas each person faces. Each case study raises issues in caring that are explored more fully, from a topic-based perspective, in the assignments in Part 3. The case studies are the imaginative core of the book and they integrate the whole text. In the assignments, students are often invited to judge the appropriateness of their proposals and conclusions by referring back to the individuals they have come to know in the case studies.

You may choose to organise an integrated learning programme from the perspective of the needs of a particular client group. If you decide to use the book in this way, an individual case study would be the starting point, backed up by the relevant assignments. This approach to using the book is particularly useful for in-service training. While the assignments and case studies interrelate in many ways, those that link directly with the case studies are listed below.

Part 3: Assignments. These 36 assignments cover those core areas common to all courses in caring and, through an integrated approach, extend beyond into a number of option areas. Child development and welfare, practical caring skills, and the hospital environment are particularly well resourced topics.

The assignments vary in length, difficulty, styles of activity and the amount of support and input the tutor needs to give. My aim has been to maintain a balance between classroom-based learning activities, and research activities that take the students out into their own environment. Where the assignments are resourced so that the students can work from the text, care has been taken to offer fresh source material. For simplicity, the term 'Task' is used throughout the assignments for all activities.

I have aimed to maintain a balance within the assignments of the four core skill areas that underpin most courses and training programmes;

- Communications
- Numeracy
- Interpersonal skills
- Problem-solving.

The style of the activities is designed to embrace the full range of assessment methods and forms of presentation favoured by the various accreditation bodies. The index will be helpful in identifying these; multiple choice, data presentation, group work, letters, role play, self assessment, posters, scale drawings etc. The NVQ index offers a guide to the vocational competences for Health Care Support Worker training that might be developed in a particular assignment.

The book has been written with the needs of *my* client groups in mind:

- for the **tutor**, a resource providing essential background in Part 1; an immediate point of reference to the key client groups and services in Part 2; flexible and adaptable learning activities in Part 3; and comprehensive indices with integral cross references.
- for the **student**, a structured way of thinking critically about the needs of clients with insight as a starting point; an information source and an approach to information gathering; job search skills; the 'How to . . .' reference section; and a direct and accessible style;
- for the **client**, a better quality of care, delivered by carers who have rehearsed practical caring skills and thought about the implications of what they do and how they do it.

Suggestions for a client group-based learning programme

1   Children and families
Case Study 1: Angela Williams
Directly related assignments
Service checklist p 34
Getting to know local services (2)
At the Well Baby clinic (4)
Milestones in child development (8)
What does a child do? (9)
Playthings (10)
Toys (11)
Children's drawings (12)
At risk? (13)
Danger at home (14)
Good food (19)
Feeding the family (20)
Warm and well (24)

2   Physical disability
Case Study 2: Andrew Neale
Directly related assignments
Service checklist p 36
Out and about in the locality (1)
Getting to know local services (2)
As others see us (6)
Good food (19)
Feeding the family (20)
Planning a future (23)

3   Mental illness
Case Study 3: Paul Weaver
Directly related assignments
Service checklist p 35
Getting to know local services (2)
As others see us (6)
Good food (19)
Feeding the family (20)

4   Learning difficulties
Case Study 4: Gladys Miller
Directly related assignments
Service checklist p 37
Getting to know local services (2)
As others see us (6)
Danger at home (14)
Good food (19)
Feeding the family (20)

Who cares?

1 The National Health Service

The NHS was set up in 1948 to provide medical advice and treatment for anyone who needed it free of charge. Before this, although some people in work paid a 'stamp' to provide some sickness benefits and doctors' fees, most people had to pay to see a doctor. They then had to pay for the treatment, services and medicines the doctor recommended. The result was that most people only saw the doctor as a last resort, and individual and public health suffered.

National Health Service Act, 1946

1 (1) It shall be the duty of the Minister of Health to promote the establishment in England and Wales of a comprehensive health service designed to secure improvement in the physical and mental health of the people of England and Wales, and the prevention, diagnosis and treatment of illness....
(2) The service so provided shall be free of charge, except where any provision of this Act expressly provides for the making and recovery of charges.

The principle of providing free and comprehensive health care to all who need it still applies today. The interpretation has changed over the years, however, as successive governments have tried to control the costs and change the organisation of the service. Before the NHS was established, seven million prescriptions a month were dispensed. By 1951 they had reached 19 million a month, and prescription charges were subsequently introduced. By 1990 prescription charges were £3.05 per item...

Britain today is very different to the Britain of the 1940s. Concerns and trends in society as a whole are reflected in the pressures shaping the NHS.

Changing patterns of illness

How has the pattern of illness changed since the NHS started?

The table and chart below give the necessary information to answer this question. The Self Check questions check your understanding as you go.

7.6 Notifications of selected infectious diseases (United Kingdom, thousands)

	1951	1961	1971	1976	1981	1983	1984	1985	1986	1987	1988
Notifications (thousands)											
Infective jaundice			17.9	7.6	11.0	7.6	7.0	5.4	4.3	4.4	6.4
Whooping cough	194.9	27.3	19.4	4.4	21.5	21.6	6.2	24.2	39.9	17.4	5.9
Measles	636.2	788.8	155.2	68.4	61.7	114.9	67.6	104.8	90.2	46.1	90.6

(Source: Office of Population Censuses and Surveys; Scottish Health Service; Common Services Agency; Department of Health and Social Services, Northern Ireland. Social Trends 20, © Crown copyright 1990)

SELF CHECK

1 What has been the trend with infective jaundice?

2 (*a*) How many cases of whooping cough were there in (i) 1951 (ii) 1988?

(*b*) Describe the pattern of illness between these dates.

(*c*) Can you think of any reasons why there were so many cases in 1986?

3 (*a*) What happened to the number of cases of measles between 1951 and 1971?

(*b*) Which years since 1971 have had the highest number of measles cases?

(*c*) Can you see a pattern in the incidence of measles cases?

(Taken from *Social Trends 20.* Reproduced by kind permission of HMSO. Crown copyright 1990)

Deaths[1]: by selected causes, 1951 and 1988

United Kingdom

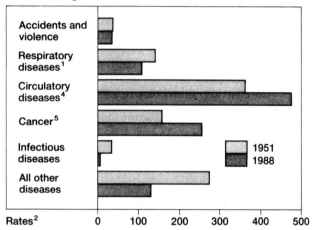

1 On 1 January 1986, a new certificate for deaths within the first 28 days of life was introduced in England and Wales. It is not possible to assign one underlying cause of death from this certificate. For the sake of consistency figures exclude deaths under 28 days.

2 Per 1,000 deaths.

3 Care should be taken when comparing 1951 with 1988 because of the change in coding procedure (in 1984). The effect of this has been to reduce numbers of deaths assigned to respiratory causes.

4 Includes heart attacks and strokes.

5 The figures for cancer include both malignant and benign cancers.

Source: Office of Population Censuses and Surveys: General Registrar Office (Scotland): General Registrar Office (Northern Ireland)

SELF CHECK

1 Roughly how many deaths were caused by infectious diseases in (i) 1951 and (ii) 1988?

2 Which diseases caused many more deaths in 1988 than in 1951? How many more?

3 (*a*) Suggest a number of causes of death covered by the term 'circulatory diseases'?

(*b*) Roughly what proportion of all deaths in (i) 1951, and (ii) 1988 was caused by these diseases?

4 Roughly what proportion of all deaths in 1988 was caused by cancer?

Did you spot the trends? You can check most of your answers to these questions by reading carefully the following commentary from Social Trends.

> Notifications of whooping cough dropped rapidly between 1951 and 1961, but there have been occasional epidemics since then because whooping cough has a three to four year cycle. The last upsurge peaked in 1986 at only 56 per cent of the level of the previous, 1982 upsurge because of increased uptake of vaccination.
>
> Measles remains the most prevalent notifiable infectious disease, though like most other infectious diseases, there is an epidemic cycle about every three years. However, as the uptake of measles vaccination has increased, the peaks of successive epidemics have been smaller. It is hoped that the introduction of the new combined measles, mumps and rubella vaccine from October 1988 will reduce the incidence still further.
>
> The chart (on p 3) shows selected causes of death for 1951 and 1988. In 1951, circulatory diseases, which include all types of heart disease, accounted for over one third of all deaths. In 1988, circulatory diseases accounted for nearly a half of all deaths. The most dramatic change since 1951 has been the fall in the proportion of deaths from infectious disease. In fact, suicide (not shown separately in the table) now forms a greater proportion of deaths than infectious diseases.
>
> The chart also shows that, in 1988, a quarter of all deaths were from cancer.

(Source: Social Trends 20 © Crown copyright 1990)

ACTIVITY

☐ Write a paragraph on how the pattern of illness has changed since the NHS was started.

The dramatic reductions in infectious disease such as whooping cough and measles have been achieved by spending money on the **prevention** of illness and disability: immunising children and child health clinics.

The killer diseases of today have different causes; personal habits, such as smoking, lifestyle choices and the environment are increasingly recognised as major causes of disease. **Health education** to promote a healthy lifestyle is an essential part of preventative health care.

People expect to be healthy

People's expectations of what health care should offer have risen since the NHS was established. In the past people took poor health or debilitating conditions for granted. Today, people expect to be healthy and go to the doctor when they think they are not.

> 'You lose a tooth for every child'.
>
> Is this an old wives' tale? Not before the NHS was established; when many now elderly women were having their families, it was quite common for relatively young women to lose all their teeth.

Why? **Ignorance** about how to prevent tooth decay, and the **cost** of dentists' fees.

Today this should be an old wives' tale. The NHS achieved this by health education about the causes and prevention of tooth decay, and a policy of providing dental care free to pregnant women and for a year after the child's birth.

The very success of the NHS in improving the nation's health is causing it problems today. Higher expectations of health have led to increased demands on the health services. Conditions and diseases are treated now for which no treatment and often no diagnosis was possible in the past. How to pay for the NHS and who should pay is the subject of on-going political debate.

What does it cost?

The NHS is big business; it is the biggest employer in Western Europe.

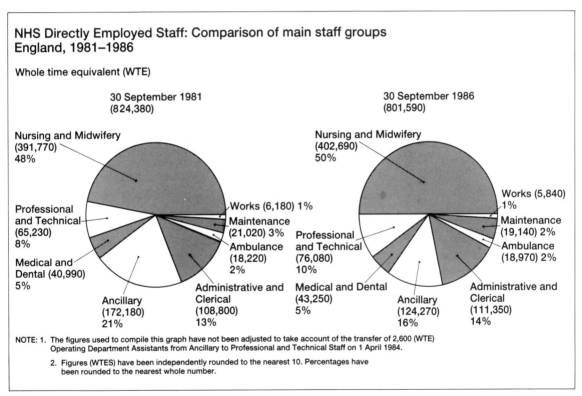

NHS Directly Employed Staff: Comparison of main staff groups England, 1981–1986

Whole time equivalent (WTE)

30 September 1981
(824,380)

30 September 1986
(801,590)

Nursing and Midwifery (391,770) 48%

Professional and Technical (65,230) 8%

Medical and Dental (40,990) 5%

Ancillary (172,180) 21%

Administrative and Clerical (108,800) 13%

Ambulance (18,220) 2%

Maintenance (21,020) 3%

Works (6,180) 1%

Nursing and Midwifery (402,690) 50%

Works (5,840) 1%

Maintenance (19,140) 2%

Ambulance (18,970) 2%

Professional and Technical (76,080) 10%

Medical and Dental (43,250) 5%

Ancillary (124,270) 16%

Administrative and Clerical (111,350) 14%

NOTE: 1. The figures used to compile this graph have not been adjusted to take account of the transfer of 2,600 (WTE) Operating Department Assistants from Ancillary to Professional and Technical Staff on 1 April 1984.

2. Figures (WTES) have been independently rounded to the nearest 10. Percentages have been rounded to the nearest whole number.

(Taken from *The Health Service in England Annual Report 1989.* Reproduced by kind permission of HMSO. Crown copyright 1990)

SELF CHECK 1   The above diagram shows two **pie charts**, so called because the various parts are shown as slices of a cake, or pie. Pie charts are a good way of showing proportion (how a whole divides up) and how proportions change. They do not, of course, show the size of the cake itself.

1   How many people in total were employed in the NHS in (*a*) 1981 (*b*) 1986?

2   In which groups has there been an increase in the number employed? In which groups has there been a decrease?

(Reproduced by kind permission of HMSO. Crown copyright 1990)

HPSS estimated gross current expenditure per head by age group (England), 1985–86

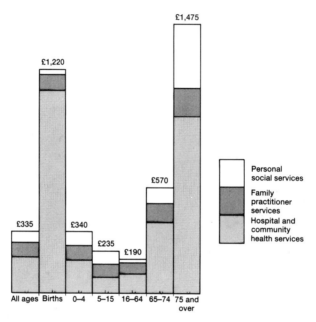

Source: The Government's Expenditure Plans 1988–9 HM Treasury 1988, HMSO

SELF CHECK 2

The above **bar chart** shows the different services used by people of each age group, and the cost of the total.

1   What is the average cost per person per year of health and social services?

2   How much does the birth of a baby cost the NHS?

3   Which age group makes the least demands on the health and social services?

4   How much more is the cost of services to a person over 75 than to a person aged 65–74? How is the largest part of these costs incurred?

SELF CHECK 3

A **graph** can convey a trend at a glance. Graphs are effective in showing changes in a measurement over a period of time, and changes in several measurements over a period of time so that comparisons can be made.

(Taken from *Social Trends 20*. Reproduced by kind permission of HMSO. Crown copyright 1990)

Capital expenditure on health

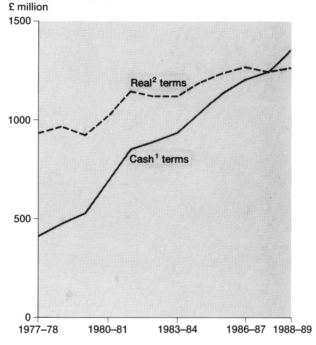

United Kingdom
£ million

1 Cash figures are based on those published in Table 14.19 of the
Public Expenditure White Paper (CM 614), January 1989.
2 Real terms figures are expressed in 1987–88 prices as adjusted by
the GDP deflator published by HM Treasury in June 1989.

Source: Department of Health

1   Describe the trend in the cash spent on capital projects in the NHS between 1977 and 1989.
2   Describe what has happened to the buying power of this cash, the 'real terms' value of the government's capital spending on the NHS.
3   When did the 'real terms' spending fall below the 'cash terms'?
4   What do you think the effect of this has been on NHS building and renovation?

Changes in the NHS

In view of the importance of the NHS as an employer and a consumer of wealth as well as the main provider of health care for the nation, it is not surprising that almost every government since the Second World War has made changes to some aspect of the working procedures of the NHS.

'Working for Patients'

This is the name of the current reorganisation of NHS services. The diagram below shows how the government intends the changes to work.

NHS STRUCTURE

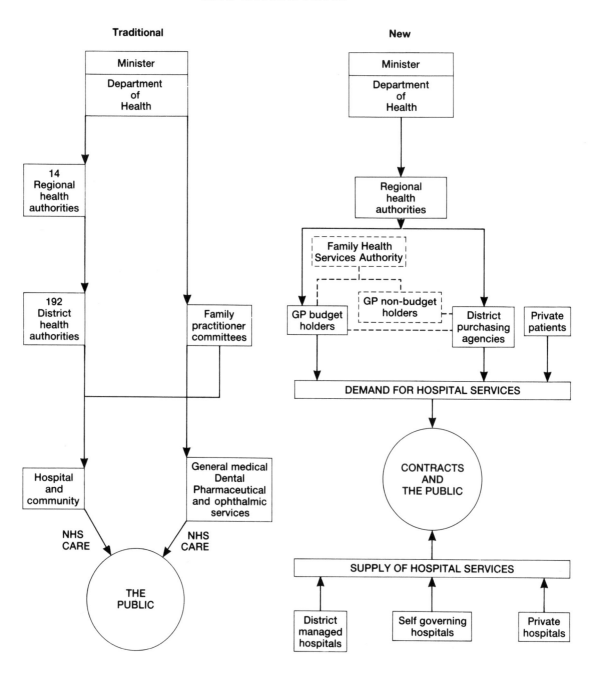

The section on the left of this diagram shows how services were organised and the philosophy of care until the 1991 changes. The Minister and the Department of Health were directly responsible for the Family Practitioner Committees which organised and financed the GP services, and for the 14 Regional Health Authorities. These were between them responsible for the 192 District Health Authorities (DHAs) across the country. Each District Health Authority provided the range of services for the people living there. Services were provided and people used them.

How did this work in practice? Mary went to the dentist for a filling, and was referred to the local district hospital to have her wisdom teeth out. Fred went to his GP who diagnosed bronchitis and prescribed antibiotics. She would also like him to have a chest X-ray and to see a specialist. The GP decided to refer him to a particular consultant she knew at a teaching hospital some distance away, not, in this case, to the local district hospital. She would write a letter of referral and Fred would be sent an appointment in a couple of weeks.

The section on the right of the diagram opposite shows the structure of the new system and the thinking behind it. Here the patient (the 'public') is seen as the starting point, making up the **demand** for health care services, and making choices, together with the GP, about the **supply**.

How does this work in practice? If Fred's GP is a **non budget holder** the practice will continue to refer patients to the local district hospital where their treatment is financed by the district purchasing agency. The district will have the task of organising the contracts to provide the various services it needs. If Fred's GP belongs to one of the group practices who have chosen to hold their own budgets, '**GP budget holders**', then the practice will have worked out its own arrangements for referral, buying some services from the local district hospital, some perhaps from a hospital outside the district, some from a hospital that has 'opted out' to become a '**self-governing trust**' and some perhaps from the private sector.

What's new?

In the traditional structure of the NHS, hospital and community services were planned and controlled by the District Health Authority (DHA). The District Health Authority's responsibility is still to its local population. The DHA now has to act as Purchaser to buy the best quality and value-for-money health care for that population. To do this, it will be allocated a certain amount of money to spend for each person (i.e. 'per capita') arrived at by calculating average costs of health care for people of different ages and social need. The chart on p 6 is an example of the sorts of figures used in this kind of calculation.

This way of looking at health care breaks the traditional relationship between the DHA and local health services; the DHA used to manage services, now it buys them. Hospital and community services on the other hand, become Providers, and have to demonstrate that their services are worth purchasing – offering good medical care, short waiting lists, facilities in good physical condition, and, at the same time, being cost effective.

Under the new system, there has to be a clear split between Providers of services (hospitals in the main) and Purchasers of services – the DHA. In theory, Provider Units have more autonomy under the new system, and are free to provide and market high quality value-for-money services. The reality is that this profound change is taking place against a backdrop of cutbacks over several years. You saw in the chart on p 7 how the 'real terms' expenditure on one important aspect of NHS funding, the capital programme, has fallen in recent years. This reorganisation reflects the thinking and values of the Conservative government that introduced it. Patients are seen as 'customers' who can choose the services they need, albeit through the GP or Purchasing Agency who does the 'shopping around' for them. Fred may not notice the difference, but his GP might feel that financial pressure led her to refer him to the local district hospital because it is cheaper, when she would have liked to refer him to the consultant she knows in the teaching hospital some way away. All health service staff – doctors, nurses and managers – are involved in a massive change in the way services are planned and delivered, and a vast increase in financial planning, information systems and paperwork.

Contrasting points of view

Shown opposite and on p 12 are two extracts showing different perspectives on the government's reforms. Read them carefully and consider the following questions.

SELF CHECK

1   Which piece aims to show the advantages of the new system? List the advantages to patients identified here.
2   Which extract aims to show the disadvantages for patients of the new system? List the drawbacks identified here.
3   Who do you think each piece is aimed at?
4   What do you think is the writer's purpose in each case? To explain? To persuade? To reassure? Pick out words or phrases from the text to support your view.
5   What is the purpose of the cartoon in each case?
6   Which extract do you find the most persuasive? Why?

Extract 1 General Practice Funding Scheme

Family doctors already play a vital role in the Health Service and they will play an even bigger role in future. From April 1991 larger practices will be able to choose to take control of some NHS funds to finance a range of local services for their own patients – including certain hospital treatments, and the cost to the NHS of prescriptions and some staff needed for the practice.

   If your GP chooses to join the practice funding scheme, what will it mean?

- The level of funds will be agreed between your GP and the Regional Health Authority. It will take into account the health care needs of all the patients on the practice list – for example, the extra requirements of elderly people, patients with special needs, the hospital services likely to be used and so on.
- Your GP will be able to use the fund to arrange the right treatment for you speedily and effectively. For example, your GP should have greater flexibility to look around for treatment in hospitals which offer the shortest waiting times. The aim is to improve the choice of good quality services available to you and your GP.
- The practice will be able to use any savings from the fund for your benefit – for example, in employing another nurse or buying new diagnostic equipment for the surgery.

So if your doctor has a practice fund, will you still get the treatment you need?

- Yes. GPs will receive sufficient funds to enable them to provide full and proper treatment for their patients. Even if the practice overspends its funds, there is no question of patients not getting the treatment they need.

So it is important that your GP thinks carefully about how much medicine you need. To help your GP prescribe for you in the best possible way, from April 1991, what is called an 'indicative prescribing scheme' will be introduced. You will continue to get the medicines and appliances you need. The scheme should cut out waste, which will mean more money is available to spend on other patient services in the NHS.

   How will the 'indicative prescribing scheme' work?

- Each family doctor practice will be able to discuss with the local Family Practitioner Committee the amount it needs for prescribing for its patients. This should enable the needs of patients who require expensive medicines or larger quantities of medicines to be taken fully into account. A practice with more patients needing expensive medicines will be set a larger amount. The amount is not fixed firmly and the doctor will in no circumstances be told to stop prescribing necessary medicines. If the doctor overspends, he or she may be asked to explain the medical reasons for this to another doctor.

Will you continue to get your prescriptions, even if the medicines are expensive?

- Of course. there will be no limit on meeting the cost of medicines or the amount of medicines that your doctor can prescribe. You can be sure that you will still get all the treatment you need from your family doctor.

(Taken from 'The Health Service – The NHS Reforms and You' published by the Department of Health)

Extract 2

(Reproduced by kind
permission of the
Confederation of Health
Service Employees (COHSE))

GP practice budgets

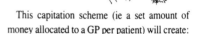

General comments

The Government proposals on GPs owe their existence to an obsession with introducing market health care at any cost.

To do this, first the Government needs to separate the provision of health care from those who supply it. That is what the white paper proposes. GPs and health authorities will buy services provided by separately run hospitals. Once this structure has been established, full privatisation will be an easy step.

Practice budgets are suggested because they create independently resourced providers who can purchase services from suppliers in the "internal market". Opted out hospitals and the private sector will then supply care bought on behalf of patients by health authorities and GPs.

Objections

The Government claims that these proposals will increase efficiency and patient choice but the reality is different.

While there is always room for improvement, our GP system is envied throughout the world. Currently, it manages 90 per cent of all episodes of health care for less than 8 per cent of NHS spending. 70 per cent of visits occur within one day of the request by the patient. It would be hard to improve on this level of efficiency and value for money.

The improvements we would all like to see in the service will certainly not be achieved by the introduction of practice budgets. Instead the Government threatens to ruin a uniquely effective service.

Effects of Practice Budgets

The Government's allocation of a fixed budget to a GP practice will mean for the first time that a practice will benefit, or lose financially, from the treatment decisions made by the doctors who own it.

This will disrupt forever the doctor/patient relationship based (until now) on mutual trust. This is one reason why the BMA is so opposed to the proposals. A patient will never know if a doctor is making a genuine diagnosis or thinking of the budget.

This capitation scheme (ie a set amount of money allocated to a GP per patient) will create:

● Incentives to increase the list size. If quality is to be improved lists should be smaller not larger.

● Strong incentives to practise "risk discrimination". That is, exchange "expensive" ill patients for "cheap" healthy ones. The more pressure there is on the budget, the greater will be the incentive.

● Problems for those careless enough to need treatment at the end of the financial year when the budget has run out.

Under this system, the "best risks" (young, fit, healthy) get more access to care than the "bad risks" (elderly, chronically sick, pregnant, disabled). This is the opposite of the NHS which offers treatment to those who need it not those who don't.

Practice budgets, combined with the new GP contract, discriminate against women doctors who often work part-time and so have smaller list sizes. The new emphasis on financial reward related to list size will make women unattractive practice partners.

This could drive many women doctors out of practice, so reducing patient choice. On average, women see their GPs four times as often as men, and many prefer to see a woman doctor.

Practice budgets will also burden GPs with huge bureaucratic responsibilities. They will be expected to shop around suppliers for "good buys", draw up and monitor contracts and monitor their own spending as the year goes on. In between all this accounting they may just have time to see some patients.

This is neither a sensible nor efficient use of an expensively trained doctor's time. ■

Extract 1 comes from a booklet *The NHS Reforms and You* published by the Department of Health. You may have discussed at length what its prime purpose is – whether it is to **explain** the changes or to **persuade** the public that the changes will result in better health care. The tone is certainly intended to be **reassuring**, using phrases such as 'of course, there will be no limit on meeting the costs of medicines . . . ' which are designed to put the reader's mind at rest.

Extract 2 has an altogether different purpose. It is published by COHSE (the Confederation of Health Service Employees) to alert its members to what it sees as the damage to primary health care the new system will bring about. Its prime purpose is also to **persuade** and it does this by putting forward arguments and supporting them with evidence. It also makes effective use of humour by including a cartoon and by using phrases such as '. . . those careless enough to need treatment at the end of the financial year . . . '

Changing care for a changing population

ACTIVITY

☐ What do the charts below tell us about what this country will need by way of care in the future?

The age structure of the population of England and Wales 1851–2021

(Source: Censuses of England and Wales and OPCS Population Projections.) Taken from *The Changing Population of Britain* (ed) Heather Joshi (Blackwell 1989))

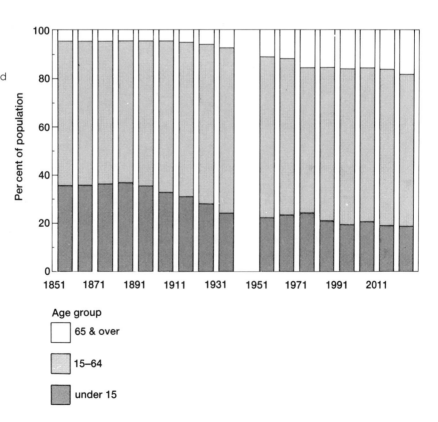

Age group

☐ 65 & over

▨ 15–64

▩ under 15

SELF CHECK

Referring to the chart on p 13:
1   Roughly what percentage of the population was over 65 in (*a*) 1851; (*b*) 1951; and (*c*) 1991?
2   What percentage of the population was under 15 in (*a*) 1851; (*b*) 1951; and (*c*) 1991?

(Taken from *Social Trends 20*.
Crown copyright 1990)

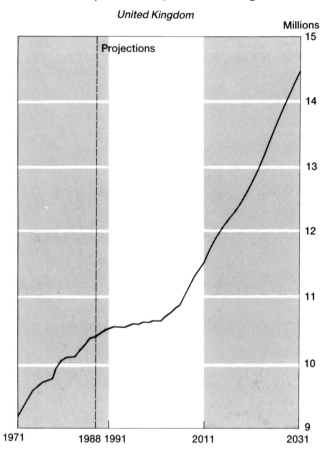

Population of pensionable age[1]

United Kingdom

1 Men aged 65 and over, women aged 60 and over.

Source: Government Actuary's Department. Office of Population
Censuses and Surveys: General Register Office (Scotland):
General Register Office (Northern Ireland)

SELF CHECK

1   How many more elderly people of retirement age were there in 1988 than in 1971?
2   How many people of retirement age are there expected to be in (*a*) 2011 (*b*) 2031?

Points to think about:

- The chart on p 13 shows the changing proportion of people of each age group in the population over the past 150 years. Remember that the population has grown massively over this time so numbers have increased. Variations of a few percentage points means millions of people, as the chart above shows.
- This chart shows the great increase in the numbers of elderly people. Remember that the chart on p 13 shows a corresponding decline in the numbers of younger people to support them.

The essential message is that people are living longer; there has been a marked increase in the proportion of people over 65 in relation to younger people over the past century. This trend will continue into the next century. As a proportion of the whole age group, very few elderly people require a lot of nursing care, but a marked increase in the numbers of elderly people, particularly of people over 85, will, of course, mean a marked increase in the number of people needing some sort of care. Health and social care planners have to ask, therefore:

1   What kind of care services will elderly people need?
2   What kind of care will elderly people want?
3   What staff do we need to provide care?
4   How do we find and train this staff?
5   What kind of care can we afford as a society?

DISCUSSION POINT   ☐   Imagine your group has to plan health services for the elderly in the year 2000. Which of the above five questions do you think you should take as your starting point?

There is no right or wrong answer to this; obviously all have to be covered. 'What can we afford?' as a starting point shows your awareness of political, perhaps economic factors in health care provision, 'Who will staff the services?' shows your awareness of the nursing shortage. The question that service providers are increasingly taking as the starting point is 'What kind of care will elderly people **want**?' and then to follow up, 'How do we achieve this?'

Most elderly people would not want to go into a residential 'home' or hospital if they could be better supported in their own homes. This is the thinking that nurses, doctors, managers and other health care professionals increasingly recognise as the way to improve the quality of life of a lot of people who have been offered either residential care or nothing at all in the past. People with a mental handicap or physical disability, people with a recurrent mental illness as well as elderly people have often had little choice but to stay in hospital for much longer than necessary because there was no way of organising or paying for the help they needed at home. The reorganisation of care in the community, 'Caring for People' to be phased in by 1993 is one response to the recognition that people are individuals; as we all have different needs, we will need different services as we get older.

Changes in nurse education and training

The recognition that there will be more frail people needing support was an important factor in Project 2000, the name of the plan to change nurse education and training. It was called this as health care professionals looked towards the year 2000 and considered questions along the lines of the five questions listed on p 15. The questions on staffing brought into focus the whole range of problems facing the nursing profession.

ACTIVITY

☐ In the following table, a number of problems affecting the nursing profession are listed on the left, and on the right are proposals for dealing with the problems. Your job is to put yourself in the position of a working party to consider what changes should be made to nursing, from student nurse training onwards. The task would best be done in small groups.
You could
● copy out the points, cut up the cards and organise them into groups of problems and proposals
● copy out the table and draw lines from problems to proposals
● copy out the problems down the left side of your page and write in proposals on the right.

This is the background to the changes in nurse education and training that have brought about the healthcare assistant as a new style of worker in the health services.

ACTIVITY

☐ Find out what your local hospital and health authority is doing to address the problems listed in the table. Which of the proposals are they acting on? Are they taking some different measures? What are they doing to implement Project 2000 in nurse training?

The healthcare assistant

New healthcare assistants join NHS drive for better patient care

The first members of a new group of NHS staff – called healthcare assistants – will begin work in hospitals and the community from this summer, NHS Chief Executive Duncan Nichol said today.

They will help healthcare professionals with patient care, leaving the more highly trained staff to deal with the work for which they have been trained. Mr Nichol pointed out that the healthcare assistant is not a completely new concept. 'There are a wide range of staff currently carrying out support tasks, for example, nursing auxiliaries, ward clerks, housekeepers, helpers to the paramedical professions, community care assistants, whose skills and experience are vital to the continued delivery of quality patient care.

The tasks an HCA might do will depend on

● the condition of patients. If a patient is stable, more activities can be carried out by an HCA, provided a professional practitioner is responsible for ensuring, monitoring and evaluating the delivery of care.

Problems affecting nursing	*Proposals*
• Student nurses seen as 'a pair of hands'. Wards are largely staffed by student nurses. • More elderly people will need care in the community. • Numbers of school leavers are falling: 25 per cent well qualified young women school leavers have traditionally gone into nursing. The size of this group is falling too. • There is a high drop out rate among student nurses – 35 per cent per year. • 90 per cent of nurses are women, whereas 50 per cent of nurse managers are men. • Of 500 000 nurses, 30 000 leave each year. On average nurses stay in nursing for six to eight years. • Many women leave nursing to have a family and never return. • Increasingly, people with a mental illness or handicap will live in the community, and need care. • Part-time jobs in nursing are usually of low status. • Many student nurses are alarmed by their responsibilities – sometimes being alone in charge of a ward. • Enrolled nurses (ENs) who went into nursing with slightly lower qualifications than registered nurses (RNs) (three O levels as against a minimum of five for RNs), are frustrated by their lack of career progression. • Women with children need good childcare if they are to work. There is currently very little childcare in NHS workplaces. • Unqualified staff, often with a lot of experience and skill, have no way of progressing into the nursing structure, so remain on low pay and low status. • Low pay often despite years of experience. • Nurses are frustrated by the pressures that stop them spending more time with each patient. As more patients are treated and discharged sooner, people in hospital need intensive care. • The shortage of nurses and nursing assistants is acute. All hospitals have job vacancies.	• Abolish the 'lower' EN status. Have a single nurse training programme. • Introduce childcare in the workplace for under 5s. • 'Clinical grading' – pay and responsibility scales to offer career progression for nurses who want to stay working directly with patients. • Change the student nurse's position so they are treated not so much as a pair of hands but as a learner with 20 per cent time on the wards. • Attract more men into nursing. • Encourage people with different qualifications to enter nursing. • Increase the numbers of community nurses. • Bring nurse education closer to training for other caring professions – they will be working more closely in the future. • More 'return to nursing' courses to update women who have taken a 'career break'. • Introduce flexibility in patterns and hours of work – even in more senior posts. • Attract and train a new worker – the 'healthcare assistant' to work under the direction of the new style 'Registered General Nurse'. The nurse will concentrate on nursing tasks and the HCA will carry out essential care of the patient. • Reward unqualified care staff with a career structure. NVQ (National Vocational Qualifications) aims to give awards by competences, as an alternative to point-of-entry exams.

- the type of care provided – for example, the care and rehabilitation of elderly people may require healthcare assistants to display a range of skills in support of a multi-disciplinary professional team. Other healthcare assistants will work mainly in support of a single profession.

Mr Nichol said: 'The term healthcare assistant will apply to staff who, while not qualified in one of the healthcare professions, will be clearly involved in the provision of patient care or in other ways in direct support of a professional group, and can demonstrate the necessary level of competence through acquiring appropriate vocational qualifications. It is intended that these vocational qualifications will enable some healthcare assistants to gain access to professional training.'

'The introduction of healthcare assistants provides the health service with a means of meeting future health care needs of the population, and an opportunity for training this group of staff.'

ACTIVITY

☐ Read carefully the above extract from a press release by the NHS Chief Executive, Duncan Nichol, and answer the following questions.

1 What sort of jobs might an HCA do?

2 Which caring tasks might an HCA undertake?

3 Which professionals do you think an HCA might work with in a 'multi-disciplinary team'?

4 What is new about the HCA?

5 Will healthcare assistants:

    (a) need a qualification to start work?

    (b) be able to get a qualification once they've started work?

    (c) be able to get into nursing?

All in a day's work

The publicity surrounding the new healthcare assistant, often does not give a clear idea of what healthcare assistants actually do. What does it mean to 'work under the direction of a registered practitioner' as it is sometimes described? Are healthcare assistants allowed to work on their own? The following article *Help from Home* shows how healthcare assistants fit into a team of health and social care professionals – a truly multi-disciplinary team at work in the community.

Help from home

Elderly people discharged from hospital are often too frail to manage at home with the normal statutory services. West Lambeth health authority's home treatment team is designed to alleviate this problem by giving intensive rehabilitative support for six weeks, with the number of care hours tailored to suit the needs of the individual. The service operates daily from 8am to 8pm.

West Lambeth health authority has a population of approximately 160 000, 14.4 per cent of whom are over 65 and 64.5 per cent of these are single pensioner households. The scheme arose because clinicians working with elderly people were concerned that there was an early breakdown following discharge, resulting in a return to hospital. Other people were remaining in hospital several weeks longer than necessary because they had insufficient help at home, rather than because they needed treatment.

The scheme is based on the philosophy of client choice and community based care for elderly people, offering an alternative to prolonged hospital care and providing the support necessary for people who are able to enjoy the benefits of living in their own homes. The care is based on a multidisciplinary team approach, with the involvement of client and carer in decision making.

Professionals in the training programme
Physiotherapists
Occupational therapists
Social worker for the deaf
Social worker for the blind
District nursing service
Continence adviser
Senior ward staff (elderly unit)
Consultant for the elderly
Nurse manager of project
St John Ambulance
Occupational health nurse
Crime prevention officer

The scheme is managed by a nurse manager who is an experienced district nurse. She is responsible for admitting clients to the project, developing care plans, mobilising and liaising with other agencies which may be involved in delivering the planned care, and managing and developing the team of healthcare assistants.

The nurse manager receives referrals from the hospital team. She assesses the client's suitability for the scheme, first with ward based assessment and then through a joint visit with the client and occupational therapist or physiotherapist to the client's home. The team's work is carefully explained to the client and to the carer if there is one.

If the client accepts help from the team and is suitable for the scheme, the client's needs are explored further with the client, carer and professionals involved and a discharge date is agreed.

The manager then arranges for the healthcare assistant who will be the main worker for the client to visit the ward. This gives time for the client and assistant to form the basis of a relationship and the assistant can also obtain relevant information from hospital staff. The manager will inform the district nurse, GP and social services about the planned discharge.

Clients are accompanied home on the day of discharge by the healthcare assistant who visited them on the ward. A high level of input is given to the client during the first two days at home; between eight and 10 hours, according to need. These first two days allow the person time to become familiar with their surroundings and to become accustomed to periods of being alone.

This is a very important part of the rehabilitation programme, as the majority of older people have been observed to suffer some disorientation when first returning home.

The rehabilitation programme begins on the third day. The healthcare assistant will encourage independence by developing the person's confidence in his or her ability to perform a wide range of personal and domestic tasks.

This is done by usual verbal instruction, sharing the task where necessary and observing only those tasks the client can do without help.

The healthcare assistant will also do shopping, taking the client along when possible. Assistants will accompany clients on other outings such as visits to the doctor, dentist, optician or hairdresser. Part of the team's work consists of encouraging the development of social skills and re-establishing social networks.

During the six weeks the client is continually reassessed at home by the nurse manager and the level of care hours is reduced as the client develops confidence and independence.

In the fourth week, if the client needs longer term support, such as a home help, the relevant area organiser is contacted and a joint visit arranged. This enables clients to say what help they will need and gives the home helps a good understanding of how much the clients can do for themselves so that the level of independence reached can be maintained. This also facilitates smooth transfer without causing clients undue stress.

Further training has been requested by the staff in post to cover such areas as the side effects of drugs, people's reactions to ageing and physical handicap; working as a team; understanding the effect of diabetes and other diseases in relation to personality change; and confusion in elderly people.

Over 14 months, 86 clients received six weeks' input from the scheme. This resulted in an average of 154 care hours per client, at a cost of £1,047 for each six week period, compared with hospital costs of £3,528 for the same period.

The response of clients has been favourable. Feedback from statutory services such as district nurses, social workers, home care organisers and GPs is also very positive. Praise for the scheme and the work and support of the healthcare assistants has been received from formal and informal carers.

There are plans to develop the service further. However, to some extent these will depend on the outcome of the evaluation and availability of funds. The favourable psychological effects and increased quality of life experienced by elderly people transferred home who have developed confidence and increased independence with the support of the home treatment team make this a positive and cost effective community resource.

Hazel Steward, who submitted the article, is nurse manager of the home treatment team.

(Reproduced by kind permission of the *Health Service Journal* (4 January 1990))

ACTIVITY

☐ From the article above, answer the following questions.

1 Who manages the 'home treatment team'? What is she responsible for?

2 When does the healthcare assistant first meet the client?

3 How much help does the healthcare assistant give a client during their first two days out of hospital? What is the main purpose of this time?

4 What is the main purpose of the healthcare assistant's help during the rest of the six week period? What sorts of activities might she do to promote this?

5 What do you think happens to elderly people discharged from hospital in areas where this sort of scheme does not operate?

6 The scheme is described as 'cost effective'. What does this mean? Do you agree?

This scheme shows one of the points at which health and social care meet. Where the professionals from the two fields work closely together, the client benefits. One certainty in the changing face of care is that this trend is set to continue. Trainee nurses and social workers will learn in the same institutions and some parts of their courses will overlap. As the number of elderly people increases, they will need services at home. As the trend to support people with a range of disabilities and illnesses in the community continues, the need for flexible and imaginative services tailored to the needs of the individuals who receive them, not the institutions that provide them, becomes more acute. Some of the changes we will see in the NHS over the next few years may be welcome – but they will not come cheap.

2 The local authority

Local authorities have a responsibility to provide essential services for people living in the area. Many of these come readily to mind – education services from nursery to adult, housing, refuse collection and, of course, social services. Local authorities provide all sorts of other services, such as libraries and noise control, street lighting and park maintenance. The diagram opposite shows the range of services offered by a typical local authority in a city. Authorities organise and group their services differently, but most will offer these services somewhere along the line.

The Social Services Department

All social services departments share the same responsibilities, laid down by law, or 'statute', to protect vulnerable groups of people and to provide services for them. These are **statutory** responsibilities. These statutory responsibilities are changed in detail from time to time by Acts of Parliament.

Most social services departments have formulated **principles** along the lines in those in the 'Service checklist' assignment on p 33–37, which shape the provision of services in their area. While some essential services are available everywhere, the precise nature and organisation of services, and who is eligible to receive them varies from one authority to another.

Voluntary agencies

Voluntary organisations are enormously important in supplementing the services of the statutory health and social services. Their schemes and style of help can be tailor-made for the needs of the group of people they were set up to help.

Local authority departments

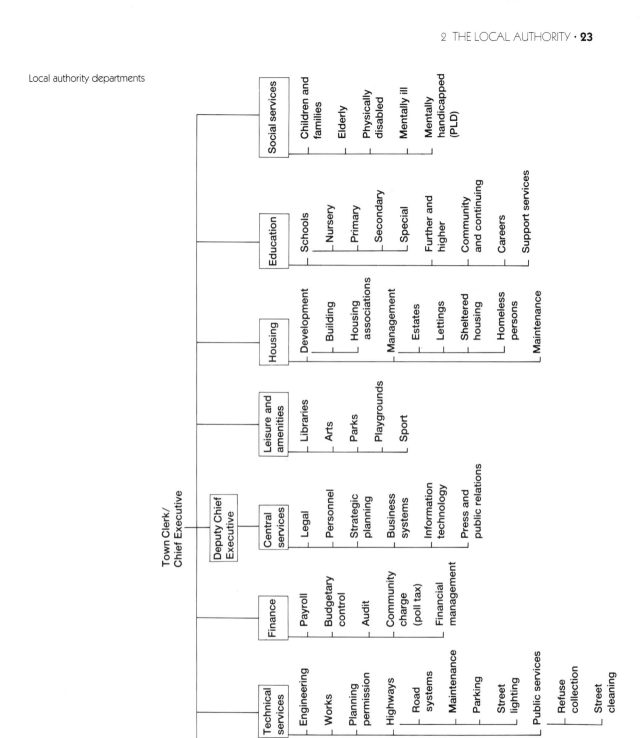

There are active voluntary organisations in all areas which can be:

- **local**, set up by local people for a particular need or scheme. Most playgroups are voluntary. They are usually set up by groups of parents who feel their children would benefit from playing with others for a couple of hours in the morning.
- **national**, a central organisation with local branches and schemes across the country. The Citizens Advice Bureau (CAB) is a national voluntary organisation with a network of local branches; Barnardo's run all sorts of homes and schemes for children in need.
- **support groups or societies** for a particular or unusual condition. These may be quite well known, such as the National Eczema Society, but often people only learn of their existence when they start to look for advice and support following a change in their own circumstances. These organisations are often set up by one or two individuals who realise that there is no organisation offering this support for a particular condition or life event. The contact address may be a private home but the contacts nationwide.

Voluntary or private?

The word 'voluntary' often causes confusion. Essentially it means 'not statutory' – i.e. not set up by the health or local authority in response to legislation, but set up because the founders saw a need for the service. It can also mean 'unpaid'. Where 'volunteers' are needed, they are likely to be unpaid, but larger voluntary organisations and housing associations employ a lot of people to run projects up and down the country. Voluntary agencies raise their money in a number of ways: direct from the public; through collections, donations and subscriptions; through grants from the government or other bodies such as the European Social Fund; through grants and working arrangements with the local authority itself, where the voluntary agency works directly in partnership. Housing Associations receive most of their money from the government-funded Housing Corporation. They all have to pay their way, and pay their staff, but they are 'not for profit' organisations.

'Private', on the other hand, means that a service is provided on a paying basis. Someone has identified a need and a market for a service, for example, a nursing home, a nursery, or a school offering expertise in helping children with particular difficulties, and decides to make it their way of life and their business.

You can see how any area has a great range of services within it. The problem for professionals in the health and social services has been to work out the best care for individuals using these different services, thought of and organised by different people, with different client groups in mind, paid for out of different budgets. Particular problems have included:

- making an assessment of an individual's needs, with the full range of services available locally in mind. It can be more straightforward to use familiar local authority services, than to enter into complicated negotiations, particularly over funding, with other agencies;

- getting the different agencies to work together in the best interests of the individual client;
- paying for different services. Sometimes a less appropriate service has been provided because money in one budget has run out, when there is still money in another, even if this service actually costs more and suits the individual less. All services have suffered from increasing financial restraint in the last ten years.

Practitioners, planners, policy-makers and the government are in agreement that the sharp division between voluntary and statutory services; between funding by the NHS, the local authority, the DSS and voluntary agencies does not always result in the best care for individuals who need and use the services. In addition, by 1990 the Conservative government was determined to move away from public provision of services to private and voluntary or 'independent' provision. The view underpinning this is that a variety of providers will result in a greater variety of services with costs kept down by competition.

This, together with the changes in nurse training and the increasing numbers of elderly people in the population forms the background to the changes introduced in the legislation 'Caring for People: community care in the next decade and beyond'.

Community care – change in progress

In the late 1980s, the Conservative government wanted to make some specific changes in how social care is brought to people who need it. These changes will be implemented progressively between April 1991 and 1993. The changes in mental health provision started to take effect from 1991; for other groups such as the elderly, the changes will be delayed, because of the huge changes in the methods of financing. There are six 'key objectives' that these changes are designed to achieve which are listed below.

Caring for people:
Community care in the next decade and beyond

1 **to promote domiciliary, day and respite services to enable people to live in their own homes wherever feasible and sensible;**
2 **to ensure that service providers make practical support for carers a high priority.** Assessment of care needs should always take account of the needs of caring family, friends and neighbours;
3 **to make proper assessment of need and good care management the cornerstone of high quality care.** Packages of care should then be designed in line with individual needs and preferences;
4 **to promote the development of a flourishing independent sector alongside good quality public services.** (Social services authorities will have the

responsibility to) make maximum use of private and voluntary providers, and so increase the available range of options and widen consumer choice;

5 **to clarify the responsibilities of agencies and so make it easier to hold them to account for their performance.**

6 **to secure better value for taxpayers' money by introducing a new funding structure for social care.** The government's aim is that social security provisions should not, as they do now, provide any incentive in favour of residential and nursing home care.

SELF CHECK

Below are some questions to check your understanding of this legislation. You may like to discuss them in your group or answer them on your own.

1 (a) What do 'domiciliary' and 'respite' mean?

(b) Suggest another word that means the same as 'feasible'. Give an example of when it might be feasible but not sensible to provide services to people in their own homes.

2 (a) Name three 'service providers'.

(b) Who are the 'carers'?

3 What needs to happen before any services can be provided?

4 (a) What do you understand by 'the independent sector'? Give two examples of services often provided by this group.

(b) What does the government see as a consequence of using the independent sector? Do you agree?

5 Why does the government want to 'clarify the responsibilities of agencies'? Suggest one good effect of this and one possible problem.

6 Suggest another term for 'funding structure'. Explain the comment in the last sentence.

What's new?

Local authorities have had to make changes in the **process** by which care is given. The local authority

- has the responsibility to make an **assessment of the needs** of each person needing care. Everyone involved should be included in the process – social worker, doctor, nursing staff, carer and any others who have a contribution to make.

- must identify a **care manager**. This is the person who organises the 'package of care' agreed in the assessment. The term 'package' is used to stress how services can be put together in a different way to meet the varying needs of clients. The care manager will often be a local authority social worker but not necessarily. Working arrangements between the local authority and health authority will vary from one area to another.

- will continue to provide services, but will also be the 'enabling authority', which buys services from other providers, voluntary and private.

Local authorities have to establish other procedures. Some of these are listed below. They have to

- monitor the quality of these services and inspect them. They must be good quality for the client and 'cost effective' – i.e. value for money
- have an effective complaints procedure for clients
- publish plans together with the health authorities on how they are going to deliver community care
- be responsible, from April 1993, for paying for people who go into residential homes whether these are run by the local authority, private, or 'not for profit' organisations
- clients are expected to contribute to the cost of their care where possible.

Changes in the structure of social services departments

The change in the way services are brought to clients means change right through local authority social services departments. The charts on pp 28 and 29 show how social services department have traditionally been organised, and how services could be reorganised – the sort of model being introduced to bring about the community care changes.

SELF CHECK

Spot the differences – the 'What's new?' section above should help.
1   How many major groupings of services are there in the traditional structure? What are they? How many are there in the new one?
2   Which is the totally new section? What do you think the tasks of the 'Inspection and registration' and 'Standards' units will be?
3   Which section is broadly the same?
4   In each system there are two sections directly responsible for services. What were these two before? What are they now?

ACTIVITY

☐   Look back at the information about 'Community Care' in this section and think about it in relation to these diagrams overleaf. Then consider the following question, first in a group discussion, then in a written answer:

What changes are local authority social service departments making in the way they organise and deliver services to clients? What do you think the effects of these changes will be to the individual in need of care?

All in a day's work

The extract on pp 30–31, 'The Role of The Care Attendant', shows Care Attendants at work and gives an outline of the training given.

Social services department 1:
traditional organisation of
services

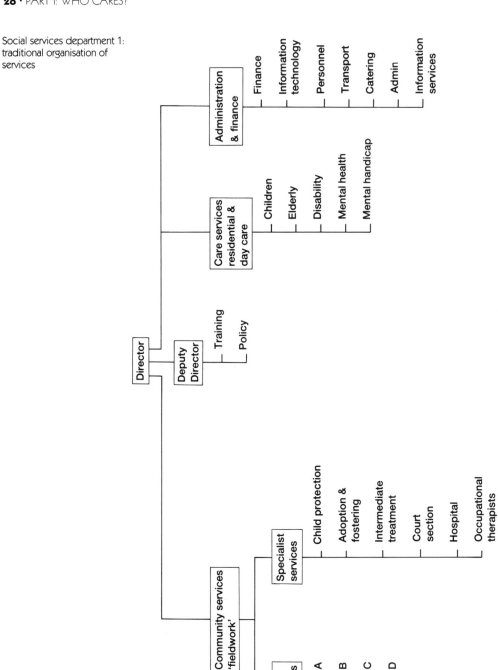

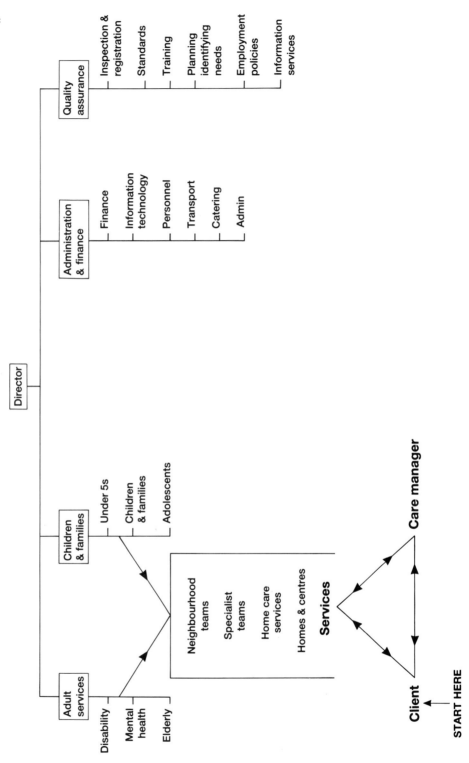

Social services department 2: possible reorganisation for community care.

The role of the care attendant

Training

The job specification for the care attendant states that the care attendants:

> 'are to provide both nursing assistance and domiciliary help similar to that which would normally be provided by the caring relative'.

The training needs of the job are concerned with:

– the physical aspects, such as bathing, toilet-care, feeding and lifting;
– the psychological aspects of counselling and coping with stress and the possibility of bereavement;
– the practical sphere, which includes a basic knowledge of relevant agencies, benefits, and so on.

During the initial six weeks of training the care attendants:

– visited old people's homes, day centres, the local branch of MENCAP and other local non-statutory groups helping and advising families;
– had meetings with staff of RAHP, community nurses, social services personnel and community mental handicap teams;
– been taught basic lifting skills, about adaptations, health and safety issues, incontinence care and welfare benefit;
– accompanied the district nurse to see the sort of people who might be helped, their home situation, the care they received.

As the care assistants became more familiar with their role they felt they should have further training in:

– caring for young children;
– caring for blind and deaf people;
– caring for the terminally ill and their families;
– first aid;
– bereavement counselling and dealing with grief.

Support

Care attendants' work is stressful and isolated. To carry it out they need support from each other and the co-ordinator. This support was mainly given at the weekly meetings held to discuss clients, work allocated, progress and problems.

A picture of the kind of help given by the care attendants emerges from the descriptions they provided of an average working day:

Care attendant A
'My day usually begins between 6.30 and 7am when I start the morning rush for the bathroom. My first job can start as early as 8 o'clock or as late as 10 o'clock. This usually involves either washing, bathing or dressing a client or a combination. This will normally take between half an hour and two hours, depending on the time allocated to that particular client.

I then catch a bus to my next job which could be preparing a lunch and warm drinks for a client left on their own all day. This completed I would then get the bus to my next address, probably eating my sandwiches on the way. We never have to worry about a drink because most of our clients are only too willing to let us make one with them.

My next task might then be to sit with a client while the carer goes out for a break, either shopping, visiting, or to the hairdressers. While we are there we do any little jobs, hand washing, ironing, sewing or anything in particular that they ask for, except for actual cleaning, because this treads on home help territory.

Sometimes the client sleeps a lot, or another may want to chat the whole time you are there. We usually make them drinks and assist them to the toilet and make them as comfortable as possible. The carer comes back feeling very refreshed and able to cope with another week of caring.

After this we may travel to another client and cook an evening meal for him, or we could meet a client off the coach from a handicap centre and make their tea and keep them company until their carer arrives home.

We then make our own way home, only to start all over again looking after our own families.

It is long, hard and tiring but very rewarding. This is not taken from any one day but a selection of the various tasks that we carry out during a routine week.'

Care attendant B

8.30–11.15: Mrs G looks after her severely mentally handicapped grand-daughter. She has angina and back trouble which is aggravated by tending to her grand-daughter who cannot move herself well and weighs about 16 stones. My job is to help Mrs G prepare her grand-daughter for a regular journey to a day centre. This involves washing and dressing her and getting her downstairs.

However, on arrival Mrs G is very ill and so after her grand-daughter has gone I carry out the various household tasks, such as vacuum cleaning and washing up. I 'phone the doctor and arrange to return when he arrives to see if Mrs G can be persuaded to admit her grand-daughter to a short-stay hospital in order to give herself a break. Then I help Mrs G to bed, make her a hot drink, pick up her pension and pay her rent at the post office.

11.15–12.00: The doctor tells her there is nothing wrong but also tells her not to lift; he leaves and her predicament has not changed. I go and get her some fish and chips.

1.00–2.00: Mrs A has multiple sclerosis and is also mentally ill, she has very limited movement. I visit to see if all is well, make lunch, keep her company and save the person she lives with a trip home from work during his lunch break. Occasionally Mrs A requires us to pick up her pension or to do some shopping.

2.00–3.00: This lady is aged 53 and she is mentally handicapped and also mentally ill. She lives alone with the support of the health service, social services and us. I am there to keep her company and help her shower.

3.00–5.00: Mrs A has had Parkinson's disease for six years. She is looked after by her husband who has help from the district nurses and us. Our tasks with Mrs A vary; she very much enjoys being taken shopping, to her sister's house, or just to a park if the weather is OK and she is feeling fit. At other times she and the care attendant remain at home while her husband goes out, when we may wash her hair.

(Taken from Care Attendant Schemes in Greater London A Survey and Redbridge and Case Study). Reproduced by kind permission of GLAD.

ACTIVITY

☐ Read the above extract and answer the following questions.

1 What are the three areas of initial training given to care attendants in this scheme?

2 What further training have the care attendants asked for? What sorts of experiences might have led to these requests?

3 How do these requests for training compare with the training requested by the healthcare assistants in the extract 'Help From Home' on p 18?

'To the person requiring help, support and care, it does not matter who they are being helped by. They just want help.'
(Photograph reproduced by kind permission of Insight)

4 How many clients does care attendant A visit in a typical day? What did each client need help with?

5 How many clients did care attendant B visit on this particular day? What sort of help did each need?

6 How well do you think the care attendant responded to the situation she found at Mrs G's?

7 What do you think are the similarities and differences between the work of the healthcare assistants in the Lambeth scheme, and the care attendants here?

Service checklist
assignment

This assignment is not designed as one to work your way through; it is designed as a prompt or review activity that can be tackled bit by bit at many points in your course. You may find it helpful to refer to the relevant section as you consider the services you would wish to suggest for the people in the case studies. The list is not comprehensive – it's hoped you will find all sorts of local variations in the range of services listed here.

Who are the clients?

Reorganisations are, or should be, about meeting the needs of people who need help as effectively as possible. Social services are organised to respond to the needs of the following groups of people, either long term, because of a particular condition or illness, or short term because of a sudden crisis.

- Children and families
- Elderly people
- People with, or recovering from, a mental illness
- People with physical disabilities
- People with a mental handicap.

Increasingly, services will be organised around the needs of these groups without the dividing line between 'residential' and 'community' or 'domiciliary'.

The following **service summaries** list the sorts of services that might be available to each client group in your area. All areas will have some of these; some might have all; and others might have their own unique schemes.

Services for children and families

(Sample) Principles

To make the safety and welfare of children paramount; to identify children at risk of physical, sexual or emotional abuse or neglect and offer them protection and care; to work in partnership with parents and families wherever possible; to offer appropriate substitute care where this is not possible.

Service	What it is	Who it is for	Who provides it
Children's homes			
Child minding			
Day nurseries			
Intermediate treatment			
Social worker			
Family aides			
Family centres			
After school play schemes			
Holiday play schemes			
Play groups			
Home finding (Fostering and Adoption)			
Supported homes for young people			
Toy library			
Health Visitor			
GP			
NSPCC Childline			
Children's centres			
Welfare rights advice			
Legal advice			
Playgrounds			
One o'Clock Clubs			
Gingerbread			

Services for elderly people

Principles

To respect the dignity and choice of elderly people using services, to enable them to enjoy the maximum independence possible, whether their choice is to live at home or in residential care.

Service	What it is	Who it is for	Who provides it
Residential homes (long-term)			
Respite care (short-term)			
Sheltered housing			
Drop-in centre			
Day Centre			
Meals-on-wheels			
Luncheon Clubs			
Special equipment			
Home help			
Care Attendant			
Welfare rights advice			
Physiotherapy			
Occupational therapy			
Pensioners Association			
Age Concern			
District nurse			
Holidays			
Hospital			
Chiropodist			
Mobile library			

Services for people with, or recovering from a mental illness

Principles

Everyone experiences stress at times of crisis. This can trigger a physical, or sometimes a mental illness. People with a mental illness should be treated with dignity and respect and be given the chance to make informed choices about their care whenever possible. Support should be offered in the community to enable independent living and to minimise the need for institutional care.

Service	What it is	Who it is for	Who provides it
Hostels			
Group homes			
Day centres			
Hospital			
Community Psychiatric Nurse (CPN)			
Social Worker			
Advocacy			
Drop-in advice centres			
Counselling			
Welfare Rights			
Disablement Resettlement Officer (DRO)			
Sheltered employment			
Adult Education			

Services for people with physical disabilities

Principles

To base services on the recognition of individual needs; to help and enable people to live a life-style of their choice, as fully and as independently as possible, in their community.

Service	What it is	Who it is for	Who provides it
Residential homes (long-term)			
Respite care (short-term)			
Purpose-built/ adapted housing			
Adult Education			
Home help			
Special equipment/ adaptations			
Occupational therapist			
Care Attendant			
Welfare Rights e.g. Mobility Allowance Attendance Allowance			
Disablement Resettlement Officer (DRO)			
Sheltered employment			
Day centres			
Holidays			
Physiotherapy			
Mobile library			
Social worker			
District nurse			
Laundry service			

Services for people with a mental handicap

Principles

To enable people with a mental handicap to secure a normal way of life, living independently wherever possible; to support and consult families and carers about their needs; to enable people to develop their potential to the maximum; to recognise their ambitions and preferences and to protect their legal and human rights.

Service	What it is	Who it is for	Who provides it
Care attendant			
Respite care			
Education			
Adult Education			
Hostel/Group homes			
Holidays			
Welfare Rights			
e.g. Mobility Allowance			
Sheltered Employment			
Adult Training Centre			
(ATC)			
Day centres			
Advocacy			
Village communities			
Sport			
Support groups			
Residential homes			
(long-term)			
Home finding			

Case Studies

Case Study 1: Angela Williams

Angela Williams lives in a flat on a pre-war estate with her two children, Ricky, aged 3 and Michelle, aged just one. She had been rehoused here a few months before the baby was born, with her partner, Des, the father of the children. She has known him since they were at school; she is 22 and he is a year younger. They were married at the time they were rehoused. They were getting on well, and having a place of their own made a big difference after living at her mum's with Ricky. Des was earning quite good money at the time, doing building, painting and decorating jobs with various people he knows, and they spent it on the flat. They got a washing machine and some furniture and made it look bright and homely, but then his job finished, the money ran out, and the rows started again.

Angela likes Des but finds him immature especially where the kids are concerned. He likes to play with them and Ricky adores his dad, but Des doesn't seem to see the need to make any changes to his happy-go-lucky lifestyle, and Angela found it like having three kids instead of two. He moved out, and now she is on her own. He drops by most weeks and is generous with money when he has any. She cannot count on him, however, either for money or for help. The gas and electricity bills last week were enormous. She had no idea how fast they could mount up – last year when Des was working it had not seemed so much but now she cannot see how she can pay it out of her Income Support. Right now if she were to have any spare cash she would spend it on shoes for Ricky – his trainers let in the wet.

Ricky is giving her a hard time, and Angela thinks he is bored at home. He has dreadful temper tantrums, and throws things around, even at her. Angela heard of a playgroup but it seems she should have put his name down a year ago to get him in; at the time Angela was too preoccupied with the baby, the new flat and Des, to think about things like that. Someone said you can only get a child into a nursery if you have a job to go to, which she would not want anyway because of the baby.

The baby is hard work too – Michelle is constantly on the go, crawling round, getting into everything. Now she is starting to walk, if ever Angela

(Posed by model). (c) Paul Hall-Smith.

takes her eyes off her, she turns round to find chaos. She empties out the cupboards and untidies as fast as Angela tidies up. Des never finished the kitchen, and Angela has removed half the doors because they were so wonky, and he never tacked in the electricity cables as he said he would. She ends up screaming at Michelle and yanking her away from the things in the kitchen and dumping her down in the hallway. If she is a bit rough, too bad, she has got to learn sometime. It was Michelle's crying all evening when she was little that drove Des mad when he was with them. She still wakes three or four times a night, and Angela comes close to hating her as she drags herself out of bed. She is constantly tired.

With everything else, she cannot face much cooking. These days she tends to pop down to the corner shop for something ready made for tea but she cannot get much when the money runs low. If she does not fancy it herself she does not bother with eating anything much. It was different when Ricky was a baby; she and her mother did not always get on, especially when Des was around, but she never had to think about food. Her mum usually cooked the evening meal and did the shopping. She was good with babies too and used to play with Ricky and babysit so Angela could go out. Now Angela lives two bus rides away so she hardly sees her mother or her friends who live near there.

A health visitor from some clinic called a couple of times after Michelle was born, and left a card with her phone number on which got lost. If Angela ever needs to take the children to the doctor she still goes over to her mother's GP where she used to take Ricky but it is a bit of a hassle, so she does not often go. Her mum forwarded her a card she was sent from the clinic there to remind her about an immunisation appointment for Michelle, but she forgot to go. She was annoyed with herself as she tries to be careful about things like that, and was regular at the clinic with Ricky when she lived in the area.

She misses Des more than she thought she would. Last summer she met quite a few other young mothers in the park at the One o'Clock club, but in winter it is cold and hardly anyone goes there anyway. One mum, Janice, lives in the same block but Angela would feel shy about asking her in. Angela realises she is lonely and thinks it will show if she asks people in. Anyway she might show herself up by shouting at the kids; she flares up so fast and she cannot stop herself. Yesterday she hit Ricky really hard after he had thrown a toy at her. He was howling and she burst into tears . . . . it worries her.

ACTIVITY 1: **IS ANGELA ALONE?**	☐ Draw a diagram to show Angela's present social and personal contacts. Take a whole side of paper, write Angela's name in the middle and draw a line out to each contact. Add a comment to show how reliable or regular these contacts are.

ACTIVITY 2: WHAT'S THE PROBLEM

☐ What do you think Angela's problems are? What could be done to help her with them? Discuss.

Divide a sheet of paper into three columns

Column 1: Problems	Column 2: Practical steps	Column 3: Who?

In Column 1, list what you see as Angela's problems. In Column 2, suggest what you think could be done to help her with these problems. In Column 3, write down who you think could offer this help.

ACTIVITY 3:
FINDING OUT

☐ What amenities are there in your area for parents with pre-school children?

What would Angela need to know in order to use the amenity; e.g. location; hours; how much it costs; is it free? how to join?

1 Using the relevant section in the 'Service Checklist' assignment on p 34 for ideas, find out:

(a) What does the **library** offer?
- story telling?
- making things?
- a play area/puzzles?
- borrowing children's books? tapes?
- information on what's on for Under Fives?

(b) Which of the following is there in your area?
- baby bounce?
- One o'Clock Club?
- park with a children's play area? paddling pool?
- animals?
- city farm?
- nature study (e.g. pond dipping)?
- half term or holiday events?
- toy library?
- sessions for children at the swimming pool or sports centre?
- mother and toddler groups?
- playgroups?
- Gingerbread group (Association for One Parent families)?

(c) What other amenities have you discovered for young children?

2 Go back to Column 3 'What's the problem?' in the table you have drawn up and add any ideas you have thought of.

ACTIVITY 4:
A PLAN OF ACTION

☐ 1 Go back to your diagram in Activity 1 and, in a different colour, add the suggestions you have made under Column 3.

2 Discussion point: What difference to Angela do you think this will make?

ACTIVITY 5:
HANDBOOK

☐ Make a booklet or leaflet listing all the services and amenities for families with young children in your area. Think carefully how best to organise and present your information to encourage young parents like Angela to get out and about and find help when she needs it.

ACTIVITY 6:
FEEDING THE
FAMILY

☐ What do you think is likely to be wrong with the diet of Angela and her children?

Look at the advice on healthy eating on pp 181–8 and draw up two lists of what Angela should try to eat more of and what she and her children should cut down on.

Make sure your suggestions are sensible – that they do not involve elaborate cooking, that children will like them and that they are cheap. Consider healthy snacks in particular. Assignments 19 and 20 on pp 181–194 take a closer look at diet.

ACTIVITY 7:
LIVING ON A
BUDGET

☐ Angela is living on a very tight budget, receiving just Income Support and Child Benefit, and with no money coming in from Des.

Find out exactly how much she is eligible to receive per week (rent aside) for herself and her two children. Work out a budget you think you could propose to her, showing

(a) how much she has to spend on food, essential household and personal supplies;

(b) how much she should put aside for bills;

(c) how much she has over for clothes and incidentals.

She still owes her last electricity bill. How much can she afford in deductions from her benefit to pay this off? Can she afford Ricky's new shoes this week? Which amenities from Activity 3 would she not be able to afford this week?

Case Study 2:
Andrew Neale

Andrew Neale had a motorbike accident three years ago when he was 22. Motorbikes were his passion at the time and he worked as a courier in London. His accident happened late one evening biking back from Reading on the M4. He suffered severe spinal injuries, and was in hospital for almost a year, first in a spinal unit, and then in a rehabilitation centre.

Andrew is now 25 and is living with his parents in their terraced house in the Midlands. He is paralysed from the waist down but has some sensation, and can manage to go to the toilet by himself. He can transfer himself in and out of his wheelchair, but cannot get around the house unaided. He can dress himself but needs help with bathing, largely, he reckons, because the shower his parents put in when they knocked

(Posed by model) (c) John Birdsall Photography

through the downstairs toilet for his use, is so cramped.

His parents were devastated by the accident, but have done their best to make him to feel at home with them. They converted their front room for him, put in the shower and installed a ramp over the steps leading down into the kitchen. Andrew can get around the kitchen but he cannot use it much beyond boiling the kettle. The surfaces and appliances are too high and the storage cupboards are awkward. The room is really too small to manoeuvre his wheelchair safely, especially when his parents are in there too.

Mr and Mrs Neale were bitterly disappointed when Andrew left school after one year in the sixth form for a job in a motorbike accessories shop. They were upset and uncomprehending when he moved to London, got a job as a motorbike messenger and lived in a squat. Mrs Neale, in particular, has had to bite back the 'I told you so' she still feels as she sees her crippled son struggling round the house in his wheelchair.

They are concerned too about the future. As they get older, how will Andrew manage? Mr Neale is approaching retirement and cannot take out the large loan he would need if the house is to be properly adapted to meet Andrew's needs. Andrew was well insured by the company, but there have been endless wrangles about Andrew's part in the accident – the route he took, the speed he was going – and, as yet, there is no sign of any compensation money.

Andrew had no choice but to go to his parents when he left hospital. He appreciates the efforts they have made to accommodate him, but is increasingly aware that he is in their front room. He mentioned to his father the difficulty loose carpets cause him and he did his best to tack them down but they are constantly being pulled out by the wheelchair wheels. Andrew would prefer bare boards, but his mother would think this a slight on her taste. He is frustrated by his powerlessness in the house – it takes all his efforts just to get around, let alone do anything in there. His mother's constant clucking grates on his nerves, and she is at home all day, having given up her part-time job after his accident. Now that he tires less quickly, he increasingly resents his lack of privacy, and feels he could manage on his own, with help for particular things. Cooking especially proves too difficult on his own – he had got keen on Indian cookery in London, but there is no way his mother would let him use those spices in her kitchen, even if he could reach the surfaces.

Andrew's mood goes up and down as he thinks about himself and his future. He knows he has become fat and flabby – too much good home cooking – and he despises his appearance when he catches a glimpse of himself unawares. He is lonely too. Quite a few of the people he was at school with still live locally, but his particular friends have, by and large, moved away. They visit when they come down for weekends, and take him out bowling or to the pub, but he feels it to be an unequal friendship – he has nothing to offer in return. As their lives take off, they come less frequently.

With Maggie it is more painful. She visited him almost every day in hospital, and stuck with him even in his low points when he was vile to her. When he moved in with his parents, however, her visits became less frequent – understandable at first as Dursford is a long way from London, and then more awkward and strained. Her zany appearance had never gone down well with his parents. His mother would make her up a bed upstairs, and the readiness with which Maggie accepted it the first time still stings. What alternative could he offer? He didn't know then and he doesn't know now.

ACTIVITY 1: ASSESSMENT

☐ **1**   Read carefully 'Activities of Daily Living' checklist below.

The Activities of Daily Living

1 Maintaining a safe environment
- comfort, freedom from pain
- avoiding injury and infection, monitoring change

2 Communicating
- verbally and non-verbally
- forming relationships
- expressing emotions, needs, fears, anxieties
- dealing with emotions, positive and negative
- maintaining an awareness of the environment
- using smell, touch, taste, hearing, seeing and sensitivity

3 Breathing
- meeting body oxygen needs
- maintaining a clear airway and lung expansion

4 Eating and drinking
- meeting nutritional needs
- maintaining a healthy diet, appropriate to the individual
- food practicalities; getting food to mouth, chewing, swallowing; appropriate presentation of food
- taking in adequate and suitable fluids

5 Body functions
- passing urine and faeces
- maintaining normal and regular functioning and control

6 Personal cleansing and dressing
- skin, hair, nails; mouth, teeth, eyes, ears
- selecting appropriate clothing
- dressing and undressing

7 Maintaining normal body temperature
- physical
- adjusting clothing and covers
- economic and environmental influences

8 Mobility
- exercising for health
- maintaining muscle tone, circulation
- counteracting the effects of immobility; relieving pressure to skin; changing position; aids to mobility

9 Working and playing
- enjoyment of recreation and pastimes
- sense of achievement, independence
- partnership in care, rehabilitation

10 Sexuality
- expressing sexuality, fulfilling needs
- reactions to intimate procedures
- reproduction

11 Resting and sleeping
- enjoying a normal sleep pattern
- taking rest as desired
- a restful environment, without stress, noise

12 Learning
- discovering, satisfying curiosity
- gaining knowledge and skills
- awareness of self as individual
- learning how to care for self and maintain health
- accepting realistic and appropriate goals

13 Religion
- according to faith and culture
- freedom not to worship or believe
- movement towards personal spiritual goals, particularly in illness

14 Dying
- as an inevitability
- peacefully, without stress, pain, anxiety
- needs met, needs of importance to others met.

(a) Which of these essential areas of life do you think Andrew now experiences difficulties with? Discuss.

(b) Copy out the 'Planning Care' chart below. Head Column 2 'Andrew's problems' and enter the difficulties you have identified in this column.

2 (a) How do you think Andrew could be supported in each of these areas, to enable him to lead as full and independent a life as possible? Discuss.

(b) Head Column 3 'A Plan of Action'. Enter your proposals for him in this column.

PLANNING CARE		
Column 1	**Column 2**	**Column 3**
The Client's Problems		
1 Maintaining a safe environment		
2 Communicating		
3 Breathing		
4 Eating and drinking		
5 Body functions		
6 Personal cleansing and dressing		
7 Maintaining normal body temperature		
8 Mobility		
9 Working and playing		
10 Sexuality		
11 Resting and sleeping		
12 Learning		
13 Religion		
14 Dying		

Andrew, too, had been doing some thinking. He has decided that he must make some changes, and has compiled a list (*see* opposite).

ACTIVITY 2: DOUBLECHECK

☐ Did you come up with the same sorts of ideas as Andrew? Check through his ideas and enter anything you missed in the relevant section of the Activities of Daily Living checklist. Did you have any ideas you would want to suggest to him?

Number 1 priority: Find a place of my own
Wait for compensation money? — No get
working on it now — Could take ages.
London? Not realistic, no way could I
get council housing.
Couldn't go back to the squat. No job.
Dursford — Council flat? Housing association
for disabled? Need advice.

Number 2: Get fit, get out
Lose weight … eat less stodge (less of
Mum's cooking)… work out in a gym?
Swimming? Sports centre has a ramp.
… adapted car?

Number 3: Money … job …
There will be some compensation, but
how much — flat, car? It won't be
enough to live off for long. I I'm to pay
my way, I need to earn… Steve worked in
computers, said I was good… Dursford
FE College? Do I need A' levels?

Number 4: Privacy esp. from Mum.
Could the district nurse come more often?
Mum said she could manage, didn't need
a care assistant. Mum misses her job
— if she could get it back she'd be happier—
more money — I'd have the place to
myself more — care assistant could come —
worth a try.

Number 5: Social Life
Ha ha. See how it goes.

**ACTIVITY 3:
FINDING OUT**

☐ **1**   Find out what services, facilities, advice and help are available to people in your area with physical disabilities. You may wish to work in pairs, to cover the full range of services and cater for different needs and ages. Start with the ideas in the 'Service Checklist' on p 36.

2   Collate and present your findings in an easy to read reference leaflet.

Case Study 3:
Paul Weaver

Paul Weaver is 46, and has suffered from mental illness on and off since his late teens. He lives in a council flat in a high rise estate. He lost his job as a warehouse cleaner after he was admitted to hospital the last time he became ill, two years ago. He now claims benefit.

He has a bedroom, a bathroom and living room with a kitchen area leading off it. The flat is dreary and scruffy but he does try to clean it occasionally. There are usually several grimy cups, with saucers and takeaway containers used as ashtrays among the piles of magazines. There are few personal possessions, but from time to time he adds to the display of pictures of landscapes and rock formations he takes from his National Geographic magazines.

Paul did well at school and passed seven 'O' levels. He only just passed his 'A' levels, however, as he became very nervous and anxious at about this time. His parents had encouraged him to take a year off after this but when he started his polytechnic course in Geography, he found he had got completely out of the way of studying and could not cope with the pressures at all. He dropped out towards the end of his first term, and shortly after this he was admitted to mental hospital for the first time. Subsequently he has had a number of admissions, once for 18 months, and has been diagnosed as schizophrenic.

Paul lived for a while in a therapeutic community, but found he could not relate to the other people there. He lived in a group home with two other men, older than himself, but this did not work out and for the last eleven years he has lived in this flat. He has a TV but at present he tends to watch whatever happens to come on the channel he first switches it to. He then switches it off when he gets bored. He does not cook much, and usually just heats up convenience food, generally tinned. He also buys takeaways – Chinese, Indian but mostly fish and chips. He smokes heavily, drinks a lot of sweet tea and the occasional can of fizzy drink.

He is coping on his own, but he is isolated, and misses his job at the warehouse. His parents have died, and although his brother in the South occasionally contacts him, they are both aware that they have little in common. Errol Johnson, the Community Psychiatric Nurse (CPN) visits him every three weeks to give him his medication and to offer support. He urged him to go to a day centre which he does now attend two or three times a week. Last September Paul enrolled at the Adult Education Institute for a course on paleontology. He went regularly at first, then occasionally and has not been at all for the past couple of months.

ACTIVITY 1:
ASSESSMENT

☐ What problems does Paul's lifestyle cause him? What could be done to help him with these problems?

Divide a sheet of paper into two columns headed 'Problems' and 'Practical Steps'. Make a list of Paul's problems and what could be done for him under the relevant headings.

This is a difficult assessment to make because you need to strike a balance between what you find unacceptable about Paul's situation and the fact that he has sustained this lifestyle for a long time.

ACTIVITY 2:
WORKING WITH
THE CBN

☐ You are attached to Errol Johnson, the Community Psychiatric Nurse who visits Paul. Errol is concerned that Paul's isolation and inactivity are getting worse. He seemed to be coping better generally before his last illness when he lost his job in the warehouse. Errol has asked you to make Paul your priority during your four-week attachment.

Errol is worried about Paul's lack of social contact and intellectual stimulation. The AEI course had seemed a good idea, but perhaps it was too demanding or stressful. Errol feels that weekends are particularly difficult for Paul. He is concerned about Paul's diet and he has noticed that the state of the flat has deteriorated recently.

Your task is to find out what provision there is in your area for people in Paul's situation.

1 Look at the Service Checklist assignment on p 35 for ideas. Start with specific services and facilities for people with a mental illness. Find out what is offered by the local authority, the health authority, and voluntary organisations. Find out where they are; address and phone number; the hours they are open; exactly what is on offer. If possible, arrange for people in your group to visit each place in pairs, and report back on what it is like. Include comments on atmosphere, and how you think Paul would react.

2 Find out about other community facilities Paul could use.

- What courses does your AEI offer? Would short courses be better than long ones? Day or evening?
- Are there any special interest groups or societies in geography, geology, or related fields in which Paul could participate?
- How do you join the public library? What goes on there?

3 Present your findings in the form of a reference leaflet. Include a map of the area, showing the locations of places and give addresses and phone numbers, and a brief summary of what each facility offers.

ACTIVITY 3: PLANNING A WEEK

☐ **1** Errol has asked you to visit Paul at some point every day for a week. Now you know what is available, can you work out a schedule of activities to propose to Paul?

2 Find a copy of *TV Times* or *Radio Times* for a week. Choose one or a maximum of two TV programmes a day you think you could interest Paul in watching. List your proposals on one side of paper, with the day, time, channel and programme and a few words of description, clearly set out.

ACTIVITY 4: PAUL'S DIET

☐ **1** What do you think is likely to be wrong with Paul's diet?

Look at the advice on healthy eating on pp 181–8. Assess Paul's diet and think about changes you could realistically suggest, setting out your notes like this:

Paul eats and drinks	How healthy?	Try as well/instead
Chinese and Indian takeaways	Very good. Lots of fresh vegetables	
Fish and chips	?	
Fizzy drinks	?	?
?	?	

2 Look back at the facilities you checked out in Activity 2. Which of these offer a reasonably priced cooked meal? If Paul followed your suggested week's activity, how many meals would he be getting? Do you want to suggest any changes?

3   What simple snacks that do not involve cooking, can you suggest? Can you improve his diet by these?

4   Draw together your thoughts on Paul's diet in the form of a weekly menu. This is not to give to him but to discuss with Errol. You want to include one hot meal a day, whether takeaway, at a day centre, or prepared by Paul himself. Include a suggestion for a simple breakfast, and another snack.

ACTIVITY 5: HOW CLEAN?

☐   Errol expressed his concern at the state of the flat but did not seem to think it a health hazard – he was more concerned about what it suggested about Paul's mental state. You feel otherwise, and are horrified at the state of the kitchen and toilet in particular. Your first reaction is to come back tomorrow with a bucketful of cleaning materials and some rubber gloves and set to work.

1   Is this a good idea? Discuss.

2   At what point does: (*a*) a dirty kitchen; (*b*) a dirty bathroom; (*c*) living area dirt; and (*d*) lack of personal hygiene become a health hazard? What particular points would you look out for?

3   In small groups, agree on an order of priority for cleanliness. Discuss in your group how you would encourage Paul to tackle the number 1 cleaning task on your list. Pool your ideas with the whole group.

ACTIVITY 6: DOS AND DON'TS

☐   Draw up a list of Dos and Don'ts for someone new to working with clients who have lifestyles and habits the worker finds difficult to accept. Present your list in an eyecatching and attractive way.

Case Study 4:
Gladys Miller

Gladys Miller has lived in Netherdene Hospital, a large old hospital for mentally handicapped people on the outskirts of the city, for most of her life. She went to live there in 1962 when she was 31. Up to that time, she had lived at home with her parents until her mother died. Her father, by then quite frail himself, could not cope on his own, and he reluctantly agreed to her moving in to Netherdene – something he had always sworn he would

never do. He died shortly after, and Gladys stayed in the hospital.

Gladys lives on Oak Ward on the first floor of the Main Building. There are twenty residents, all of whom have learning difficulties. Until a couple of years ago, the beds were arranged in two rows of ten, dormitory style. Then some partitions were made to divide the ward into sections with four to six beds, each with a locker and curtains around it. Gladys likes the change. The curtains in her section have green flowers on them. She likes the flowers but prefers the yellow flowers in the next section.

Gladys' day

7.00 She gets up, with the rest of the ward. She washes and dresses herself and then helps May, who sleeps in the bed next to hers. May always gets muddled with the sleeves, and they laugh about that. Gladys sometimes gets her own buttons done up wrong, but the nurse helps her with this.

7.45 Breakfast, Gladys counts out the knives, forks and spoons for each table - five tables of four people - and helps May eat her breakfast. May finds it difficult to keep the food on her spoon or fork. Then she straightens her bed and watches TV. Once a week nurse checks her blood pressure - she has high blood pressure for which she takes medication.

9.15 She leaves for ITU (Industrial Therapy Unit) which starts at 9.30. They package things for the airport nearby; packets of pepper and salt, packets of plastic cutlery - knife, fork and two spoons. She gets 50 pence per session she works here. She usually sits with Monica and Sal, and sometimes Brian and Joe sit with them. They don't talk much except at the tea break. Gladys does not take sugar in her tea - she knows she must not because of her diabetes.

12.00 Gladys goes back to Oak Ward for lunch. The tables are already set, and lunch is served from trolleys onto plates, distributed by the staff. Gladys doesn't get the pudding today, because it's jam roll, and she can't have that because of her diabetes. She takes the dirty plates from her table to the trolley. Then she sits in the day room and dozes in front of the TV.

1.30 Back to the ITU.

3.30 Gladys comes back to Oak Ward. The tea is ready in the urn when she gets back. Gladys carries the tray of blue plastic cups to her section, and helps May drink hers. She then goes back to the day room and sits.

5.30 Supper time. Gladys counts out the knives, forks and spoons for each table - five tables of four people, and helps May with her supper. She then takes the dirty dishes from her table back to the trolley, and goes to sit with May in the TV room.

7.00 Three evenings a week there is Social Activity in the Recreation Hall. She likes to go to this, but she finds the stairs difficult, and sometimes she feels she's been up and down them enough times already in the day. So she watches TV until

9.00 Sleeping pill, get ready for bed, help May with her sleeves and bed. Lights go out at 9.45pm.

This has been the pattern of Gladys' life for the past 30 years.

<table>
<tr>
<td>

**ACTIVITY 1:
THINKING ABOUT
GLADYS**

</td>
<td>

☐   **1**   Do you think this is a satisfactory way of life for Gladys? What has Gladys lost by living her life in Netherdene? Are there any positives? List the positive and negative aspects of life in Netherdene.

      2   Do you think she would enjoy, or could cope with, a different setting?

</td>
</tr>
<tr>
<td>

**ACTIVITY 2:
TIME FOR A
CHANGE**

</td>
<td>

☐   Look back at Part 1 which describes the changes in thinking about how best to meet the needs of people needing long-term care. Make notes on the following two questions:

      1   In what ways is care for people with a mental handicap changing?

      2   What has brought this change about?

</td>
</tr>
</table>

Change for Gladys

A new nurse, Anil Siva, came to work on Oak Ward. He felt that the ward was run according to a **routine** that the patients had to fit into and that did not take into account their individual needs, abilities and preferences. He was particularly struck by the many things Gladys could do well. At the same time, a new doctor started on the ward, and saw Gladys on her ward round. She saw Gladys to check her blood sugar levels for diabetes, and monitor her medication for her high blood pressure. She, too, was impressed by how much Gladys seemed to understand about her medical condition. Anil Siva decided to initiate an **assessment**, the first step to drawing up an **individual preparation plan** for a move into living in the community for Gladys.

The preparation plan in action

Anil has now assembled the core of a multi-disciplinary team with an interest in Gladys;
- himself (a Registered Nurse for the Mentally Handicapped – RNMH)
- Dr Joanne Leahy (Registrar)
- Ms Jenny Anderson, psychologist.

The hospital is developing a number of initiatives to move people with learning difficulties into small homes in the neighbourhood. Gladys is selected to be one of six residents to move to 6 Firbank Road. The house is about a mile away. It is owned by Outlook Housing Association which works closely with Mencare, the voluntary association that will be running and staffing the house.

      The aim of the staff at the hospital is to prepare Gladys for living in an ordinary house in an ordinary street, with 'housekeeping' support, not nursing care.

      The hospital is developing a systematic way of assessing people's abilities as a basis for devising a programme of support to help people develop the skills they need to live – and enjoy living – in the community.

ACTIVITY 3

☐ Below is an extract from the 'Long-term care assessment' form which the multi-disciplinary team agreed to complete for Gladys. Your task is to complete it with a partner, ticking the column you think best describes Gladys' ability on each item. Base your assessments on the information in the Case Study and make sensible guesses about the skills Gladys is likely to have where you do not have the precise information. Write 'N/A' where the point does not apply to Gladys; do not leave gaps.

Long-term care assessment			
	Performs activity without problems	**Needs help/prompting (State who from)**	**Does not carry out this activity**
Section 4: Self care			
1 Keeps self clean			
2 Copes with menstruation			
3 Shaves self			
4 Dresses self			
5 Dresses reasonably tidily			
6 Dresses appropriately to the weather and situation			
7 Changes clothes regularly			
8 Keeps clothes clean (washes them regularly)			
Section 5: Domestic skills			
1 Eats and drinks appropriate quantities			
2 Eats a reasonably balanced diet			
3 Makes tea/coffee			
4 Makes snacks			
5 Cooks for self			
6 Safe in the kitchen			
7 Table manners reasonable			
8 Keeps accommodation/ room clean and tidy			
Section 6: Cigarettes			
1 Buys own cigarettes			
2 Budgets for cigarettes			
3 Does *not* cadge or pester for cigarettes			
4 Deals with cigarettes safely			
Section 7: Community skills			
1 Goes out of ward alone			
2 Goes out of hospital alone			
3 Crosses roads safely			

Long-term care assessment			
	Performs activity without problems	**Needs help/prompting (State who from)**	**Does not carry out this activity**
4 Uses/can use telephone			
5 Basic reading			
6 Basic writing			
7 Can tell the time			
8 Can use public transport			
9 Shops for small personal items			
10 Shops for food and domestic items			
11 Shops for clothes			
12 Uses GP/medical services			
13 Collects benefit/pension from PO			
Section 8: Money			
1 Budgets money for small purchases			
2 Budgets for day to day personal purposes			
3 Budgets money for food and domestic purchases			
4 Budgets money for bills etc			

**ACTIVITY 4:
A PLAN OF ACTION**

☐ Look back at the picture of Glady's abilities and needs you have built up through your ticks on the assessment form.

Which areas do you think Gladys is most competent in? What is she going to need most help with? Discuss.

Now turn this assessment into an action plan.

1   Take each section in turn. Decide which skills are *essential* for Gladys to develop *before* she moves into Firbank Road. Copy out the Individual Action Plan shown following this Activity, and list these essential skills under the first column.

2   In column 2 suggest *how* you think Gladys could learn each skill, and *who* might be the best person to help her learn it.

Compare your proposals with those made by other people in your group.

Find out from your local hospital, tutor or other care workers and professionals whether your suggestions are realistic.

INDIVIDUAL ACTION PLAN SHEET

Name: _____ *Age:* _____

Current accommodation: _____

Community Housing Planned: _____ *Keyworkers:* _____

	Areas to develop before moving	How to learn Who to help	Continuing support needs	How to offer Who to help
1 Mental state				
2 Medication				
3 Physical health				
4 Self care				
5 Domestic skills				
6 Cigarettes				
7 Community skills				
8 Money				
9 Day time activities/ work				
10 Leisure activities				
11 Social activities and contacts				
12 Other				

On the move in Netherdene

Meanwhile, Gladys' life in Netherdene is changing in little ways. Anil Siva is concerned that all residents should exercise individual choice where this is possible, and he has made small but significant changes on the ward;

- residents can get up between 6.30 and 8.00 and breakfast follows on from this;
- the furniture in the day room is arranged in groups round low tables, not automatically facing the TV;
- some residents, including Gladys, have been encouraged to go into the serving area and use a kettle and tea bags to make tea whenever they like;
- more social activities take place on the ward;
- staff encourage residents to go out, and offer to accompany them to walk and sit in the grounds.

In addition, Gladys goes to the Occupational Therapy homemaking unit two mornings a week instead of ITU, followed by lunch with the other five residents who will be moving with her to Firbank Road. She has been on a number of trips with Debra, the Occupational Therapy aide, some on her own, some with Sal. They have taken the bus to the High Street, had a cup of tea and taken the bus back again. Gladys handled all the money. They have been out and looked at the shops. They looked at wallpaper patterns in a DIY shop for ideas. Gladys has chosen the wallpaper for her room, pale blue with little yellow flowers. They went into 6 Firbank Road and looked at the bedrooms now the builders have nearly finished. They walked from Firbank Road to the doctor's surgery to the Post Office and looked at the little shops nearby. Gladys bought some cigarettes and Sal bought some sweets and a hair slide. Next week, they will go to the house on their own and Debra will meet them there . . . .

Moving in

The house was due to open in the first week of April, but the opening was delayed because of problems with the builders. During this time Gladys became very agitated and restless. She also became forgetful and several times lost her concentration when she was making tea, losing interest and leaving the kettle or pouring cold water onto the tea bag. The staff were concerned that she seemed to be losing her confidence and she kept saying that she did not want to go and she did not want to leave May. Anil explained that things were changing for May too, but not as fast . . .

Gladys, Sal and the four other residents moved in on 22 May, five weeks later than originally planned. The ward staff and senior managers joined the house staff and residents to celebrate the move with a party the next day, and life started to take its new shape.

How does it work?

The residents: the residents were chosen for their compatability; they are not difficult characters, sleep well at night and are expected to adapt well to a settled lifestyle in the community.

House staff: there is a care assistant in the house at all times. One will sleep over after the afternoon shift, and another arrives at 7.00 am. They are supported by the Homecare Manager, a social worker who visits regularly. The care assistant's job is to help and support residents in their domestic lives and remind them about things they are responsible for, such as like appointments, medication. The job description of the posts at 6 Firbank Road are on p 259. Gladys can look after herself well but the care assistant is there to check the buttons. Gladys helps in the kitchen, not only laying the tables as she did before, but with preparing vegetables and making tea for herself and others.

Money: the residents draw their Income Support from the local Post Office. Gladys is over 60, so she draws her pension. Rent is paid direct to Outlook Housing Association.

Health care: The District Nurse visits one of the other residents once a week. Gladys has her check-ups at the hospital. When the residents are ill, the care assistant phones the GP for an appointment or a visit.

Day time activities: The residents do different things. Gladys takes the bus back up to the hospital and goes to ITU three days a week. On other days she helps in the house, goes for a walk to the shops, and is often quite content in her room and around the house. She may join a luncheon club or go to a different day centre in the future. At first, she went to a few Social Activity evenings at the hospital, but now prefers to stay at home except for special events. After ITU she often goes to visit May on Oak ward. Gladys is hoping that May will come and visit her in her new home soon.

Continuing care

Gladys's move to 6 Firbank Road has been a great success and by now you will appreciate that a great deal of careful thought and planning went into making it a success. That is not the end of the story, however. Gladys was not capable of a fully independent life when she went into Netherdene all those years ago, and since then she has led a very sheltered and institutionalised life. She needs **continuing care** – not nursing nor medical care, although she has conditions for which, like many other people, she needs medical supervision and occasional treatment. She needs support in day-to-day living and a **care assistant** or **healthcare assistant** can support her in this way.

Now we have to assess what her continuing care needs are.

ACTIVITY 5

☐ Refer back to the Individual Action Plan sheet. You have already completed columns 1 and 2. Now, in discussion with a partner, complete columns 3 and 4, 'Continuing Support Needs' and how to offer this support. You need to consider

1 which skills you think she needs to continue to develop after moving to Firbank Road, and how to do this;

2 which skills you think she will not be able to develop and the sort of support she needs as a result.

Case Study 5:
Mrs MacDonald and Mrs Hill

Mrs Rose MacDonald is 72. For the last year she has lived with her daughter Liz Hill and her family. Liz decided to bring her mother to live with them after a recent visit to Scotland when she found her mother confused and distressed. Liz Hill had been increasingly worried about her for some time, and on this visit the neighbours approached her with their concerns for her mother's safety. Rose wandered in the streets, was vague and often did not seem to know them when they called, and appeared not to be eating or taking care of herself or the house. Liz was aware that there was little she could do while she lived so far away as the family had all moved South.

Mrs MacDonald seemed much better after a few weeks with Liz's care. She did not seem to miss her home too much, although she often talked about the neighbours as if she was still there. She got into the way of walking to the corner shop in the afternoon and is actually reasonably fit and physically healthy.

However, Liz is aware that her mother now needs care for different reasons. She still enjoys walking but often she cannot find her way back home. Liz needs to coax her to eat meals she has prepared for her; at first she would politely explain that she'd just eaten thank you, but would feed herself slowly while Liz chatted her along. Now she rarely eats if Liz leaves her dinner for her, and her complaints that it is not cooked properly weary and depress Liz.

Mrs MacDonald is beginning to need help to dress. Recently, Liz got back from work to find her mother half undressed, vaguely looking for her clothes, which she then found in unlikely places around the house. A couple of weeks ago she found her mother's wet underwear in the cupboard under the sink. One night last week, Liz woke and went downstairs to find her mother fully dressed, trying to make a cup of tea – she had put the electric kettle on the gas, and was talking about catching the train home.

Liz Hill is now feeling the pressure. She has three children, Rosanne aged 13, Patrick 10 and Rob 7, who all demand a lot of her time and energy. Because they lived so far away, the children did not know their grandmother very well, but Liz had felt that the family would manage – Granny

(Posed by model) (c) John
Birdsall Photography

Mac had always had a wicked sense of humour that children loved. Recently, this too has begun to change; Mrs MacDonald is often irritable towards her and the children, who feel that she is being unfair to them. She is particularly critical of Rob and has quite unrealistic – and uncharacteristic – expectations of how a seven-year-old should behave. Despite herself, Liz Hill finds herself getting angry with her mother.

Liz has a part-time job as secretary at her children's primary school. She used to work in the mornings, but has changed to afternoons, from 12.30–4.00pm. It is less convenient; the children finish at 3.30, and Rob gets bored waiting for her, but it means she can organise her mother for the day after she has got the children to school. John Hill is a senior sales rep for a firm of shopfitters. He works long and irregular hours, and often arrives home late and tired.

He supported Liz's decision to bring Mrs MacDonald to live with them, and converted his workshop downstairs to make her a small but cosy bedroom. He is now concerned about the burden on the family: Rosanne's arguments are distressing to both of them; Rob's behaviour has become unpredictable and he is not making progress with his reading. Liz cannot give him even 15 minutes of her full attention after school and she is tense and irritable. John feels they need a holiday as a family, but Liz snaps at him when he mentions the summer as she cannot see how she will ever get away. They are now both feeling that they have taken on more than they can cope with.

ACTIVITY 1:
WHAT'S
HAPPENING?

☐ Look at the extract from the factsheet below. Which of the typical symptoms of Alzheimer's Disease is Rose MacDonald suffering from?

Alzheimer's Disease — What is it?

ALZHEIMER'S DISEASE (AD) is a physical disease which causes a progressive decline in the ability to remember, to learn, to think and to reason. It was first described by Alois Alzheimer, a German neurologist, in 1907.

The disease is associated with abnormal function of brain cells. The characteristic changes within the brain can be seen under the microscope and these are commonly known as tangles and plaques.

The term dementia is used to describe conditions that result in the progressive loss of mental functions. AD is the commonest form of dementia and is responsible for about half to two thirds of all cases. The next most common cause is multi-infarct dementia. This form of dementia occurs because the blood supply to tiny areas of the brain fails so that there are infarcts or dead patches.

SYMPTOMS: The symptoms of AD vary from person to person and, at first, they are not always distinguishable from the forgetfulness that occurs with being depressed, bereaved, under stress, anxious or with gradual ageing.

The loss of short-term memory is an early and most striking sign. Disorientation, confusion

with time and place, sometimes leading to the inversion of day and night, and wandering are often symptoms. As AD progresses the loss of the ability to think and reason becomes more and more marked. Simple tasks (like tying shoe-laces or telling the time) can become impossible. As the disease takes hold, victims become increasingly less aware of their condition – though they can still experience anxiety and distress. The course of the disease varies from one person to another. The decline can be rapid in some people, gradual or uneven in others. In all cases the family and friends of sufferers are put under enormous strain.

(Reproduced by kind permission of the Alzheimer's Disease Society)

ACTIVITY 2:
WHOSE PROBLEM?

☐ Make a list of the problems Mrs MacDonald's behaviour presents to herself and to others. Use a whole side of paper, or, if you are working in a group, a flip chart. Set it out in two columns like this:

Behaviour	**For whom is this a problem?**
Being irritable	for Liz Hill
	for children, esp Rob (7)
	for herself (?)

ACTIVITY 3:
ASSESSING NEEDS

☐ **1** **What are Mrs MacDonald's needs?** Identify times of day and activities where she needs help.

2 **What are Liz Hill's needs?** We know that the Hill family, Liz in particular, is under pressure and that they are wondering if they can continue to care for Mrs MacDonald.

(a) Draw up a timetable of Liz Hill's day from when she gets up to when she goes to bed. You may need to add to the information given. Remember she is the one who runs the family – cooking, shopping, cleaning, helping with homework etc.

(b) Identify the times of day when Liz Hill is under particular pressure to meet her own, her family's and her mother's needs. Can you suggest any ways in which this pressure can be relieved?

(c) What do you think about John Hill's idea of a family holiday? Is there any way this could be arranged? Do you think any other breaks would be possible to arrange?

ACTIVITY 4:
FINDING OUT

☐ **1** What services are available in your area to meet the needs you identified in Activity 3? Look back to the 'service checklist' on p 35 for ideas to start you off.

2 When you have identified a service you think might be helpful to the family, find out who you would contact for the service, names, addresses and phone numbers.

3 Draw up a schedule of a typical day for the family, adding the services you would like to offer them.

ACTIVITY 5:
THE REPORT

☐ Write a short report in which you outline the services you would recommend for Mrs MacDonald and the Hill family. Explain briefly your reasons for each recommendation.

ACTIVITY 6:
CARRY ON CARING?

☐ **1** The Alzheimer's Disease Society offers advice and support to carers. Look at the practical suggestions in this leaflet shown overleaf, and select from it the 20 suggestions you think could be most helpful to Liz Hill in caring for her mother.

2 Are the suggestions and support services you have proposed sufficient to enable the Hills to continue to care for Mrs MacDonald? Should the family make any major decisions? For example, should Liz Hill give up her job? What would be the consequences of this? Discuss.

Alzheimer's Disease Society

MEMORY, THINKING AND CONVERSATION

1. Remember the importance of good communication. Ensure that hearing aids, glasses, dentures etc are in place and working.

2. Speak clearly, slowly and simply.

3. Use 'body language' (touch, gesture etc.) to help communicate. Dementing patients are often surprisingly sensitive to this.

4. Make sure that clocks, calendars, room signs are easily seen. Remember that four clocks all telling a different time would confuse anyone. One clock with the correct time is all that is necessary.

5. Draw attention to these memory aids.

6. If you are talking about the past ensure that it is not confused with the present.

7. Try not to go along with confused thinking. Correct it tactfully if possible or change the subject. This is sometimes very difficult, especially when the patient is upset. You may be able to pacify the person, without going along with confused thinking, by saying something like "I can't see anyone in the room, but I know you can and it must be very upsetting for you." This acknowledges the fear without going along with the confusion.

8. Deal with repeated questions with as much tact and patience as you can.

9. Tell the sufferer what is going on and what is happening next. It may be necessary to repeat this several times.

10. As far as possible let them do what they enjoy doing.

GENERAL APPEARANCE, HYGIENE AND DRESSING

1. Some sufferers need reminders about hygiene as they simply forget whether they have bathed or shaved.

2. Even if the patient cannot carry out the whole task alone allow them to do what they can. Take things a step at a time.

3. For safety reasons some supervision of bathing and shaving is desirable. Make the occasion as pleasant as possible.

4. Use bath aids. Contact the Social Work Department or the Health Board.

5. Compliment the patient on his/her clean and tidy appearance.

6. Take a woman to the hairdresser. This is a morale boost.

7. Select clothes which the patient likes wearing.

8. Lay out clean clothes in the order they are put on.

9. Remove from sight any clothes for washing.

10. Simplify clothing. Use slip-on shoes, replace buttons and zips with Velcro.

WANDERING

Wandering constantly from one place to another with no apparent purpose is very common in the confused elderly. It may be partly the result of confusion and partly lack of stimulation.

1. Try distracting and coaxing the person rather than confronting them.

2. If the sufferer wanders a lot install locks that are difficult to operate. A lock at the bottom of the door, where the sufferer is less likely to look for it, can be effective.

3. Even with precautions wandering may continue. Learn to tolerate it.

4. Have an identity bracelet made for the sufferer. Do not have the address printed on it. A name and telephone number are sufficient.

AGGRESSION

1. Try not to interpret the anger as if it came from a healthy person. Anger from a brain-damaged person is often exaggerated.

2. Keep calm. Anger may be intensified if you respond angrily. Count to ten (or twenty) before saying anything, and then try to distract the sufferer.

3. Remember that forgetfulness is an advantage in these situations. Once the outburst is over the sufferer will usually forget what has happened.

4. Try to avoid 'touchy' subjects.

HEALTH AND SAFETY OF CARER AND PATIENT

As the patient's ability to reason and remember decline, more everyday situations become a potential hazard. It is often difficult to decide how far to restrict the person's freedom in order to prevent risks. You cannot remove all the dangers. A certain degree of risk is inevitable if freedom and independence are to be retained for both parties.

1. Check the house for hazards, eg trailing wires, faulty electrical appliances, access to gas appliances, loose rugs or carpets, low glass tables. Make sure medicines, cleaning fluids, paint, bleach etc are all out of reach.

2. Supervise the consumption of medicines and drugs. Keep medicines in a locked cupboard and keep a record of what has been taken.

3. Looking after someone with dementia is exhausting. You must take care of yourself and work out some 'survival strategies'.

4. Don't keep the problem a secret. Tell those close to you so that you can share it. Dementia is a distressing illness but also a common one. People may understand and sympathise more than you expect.

5. You are an individual with interests and needs of your own. Try to retain old acquaintances and spend time with them. This may mean taking time off from caring. There may be a sitting service in your area.

6. Try to 'switch off' at home when things get on top of you. Go to another room and read or just sit alone for a short time. The patient will probably not notice your absence and you will feel better.

7. Consider joining a self-help group where you will meet other people in the same position.

8. Be prepared to accept that there comes a point at which you can no longer cope and admission to hospital is necessary.

(Reproduced by kind permission of the Alzheimer's Disease Society)

Case Study 6:
Mrs Nellie Taylor

Mrs Taylor is 83, a lively and independent person. Her husband was an architect and died 25 years ago of a sudden heart attack just as he was about to retire. She lives in her own home, a spacious four-bedroomed house in which she and her husband brought up her family. It is not centrally heated as Mrs Taylor does not like central heating.

She has three children, two sons and a daughter. The eldest son, Andrew, is also an architect and lives in the West Country. His wife works and they have two grown up children. Patricia and her husband live in Brussels; he has always worked abroad. Graham is an accountant and works in London in the City. He visits once a fortnight and phones at least once a week. Mrs Taylor is, understandably, proud of their success, but it means that they are busy and do not see as much of her as she would like. Several of the grandchildren now live in London and do visit, but not regularly, although Anne quite often pops in on a Thursday after work. She was, and is, a 'favourite granny' and they used to stay with her as children and discuss their problems with her as teenagers.

She is well known and respected locally – the shopkeepers know her by name and neighbours greet her in the street and sometimes look in. She has always managed well at home, doing her own shopping and cooking. She employs Doreen O'Brien, now in her sixties, to help her with her cleaning and laundry two mornings a week.

She has found recently, however, that she is becoming more isolated as her friends die and she goes out less than she used to, particularly in winter. The telephone can be distressing – she feels she has to hurry to get to it in time, and panics when she cannot find the light switch, and she has to strain to hear. She finds she is becoming a little forgetful – last week Mrs O'Brien got the impression that she was not expecting her on her usual day, and she found that Mrs Taylor had put the butter in the oven. They laughed about it at the time but it is worrying them both.

When Anne visited last week, Mrs Croft next door caught her as she was leaving to tell her about a time last week when some teenagers brought Mrs Taylor home. Apparently she had approached these complete strangers, told them her address and explained to them that she had forgotten the way home. Once home she had made them welcome with tea and biscuits. The teenagers had knocked on Mrs Croft's door at nine o'clock at night to say what had happened.

Now in October, she is dreading the long evenings. Mrs O'Brien makes

up the cosy stove, and makes sure there is enough coal in the scuttle, but
Mrs Taylor often lets it go out. She tends to light the oven and leave it on
instead. Cooking just for herself is becoming an effort and some days she
does not bother. Mrs O'Brien often is not sure whether she has eaten or
not. She says 'Oh no, thank you, but I had a lovely breakfast', when she
offers to cook for Mrs Taylor, but she does not see any evidence of cooking.
In the past she always ate well and liked good food. She and her husband
used to eat out on special occasions and until quite recently she would
enjoy treating a grandchild.

In herself, Mrs Taylor is a fine looking, dignified old lady, now a little
frail. Clearly, she and her husband enjoyed good things; solid furniture,

fine china, books and music. They were happy together, and she finds she is missing him more now as she gets older. She is beginning to dread the future.

ACTIVITY 1:
ASSESSMENT

☐ Does Mrs Taylor need help from the caring services to enable her to continue to live an independent life? Discuss.

1 Draw a diagram showing all Mrs Taylor's present contacts as far as you can tell from the information. Take a whole sheet of paper, put Mrs Taylor's name in the middle, and draw a line out to each contact. If you are working groups, you may like to use a flip chart.

2 Show on your sketch how regular her contacts with each person is. Who would notice if she needed help? Who could offer practical or regular help?

Write a paragraph in which you give your views on the assessment question.

ACTIVITY 2:
ANTICIPATING
NEEDS

☐ **1** Discuss the following points:

(*a*) Do any aspects of Mrs Taylor's present circumstances cause you concern?

(*b*) What problems do you think might arise in the near future?

What could be done to help her with these problems?

Divide a sheet of paper into three columns, headed 'Problems', 'Practical Steps', and 'Who?'

2 In Column 1, first list the problems you think are affecting Mrs Taylor now and then list those you anticipate might arise soon. In Column 2 suggest what you think could be done to help her with these problems; and in Column 3, write down who you think can offer this help.

ACTIVITY 3:
FINDING OUT

☐ Which services are available to elderly people in your area? Look at the Service Checklist assignment on p 35 for ideas. Find out what **statutory services, health services** and **voluntary services** offer and **how** to contact these services.

ACTIVITY 4:
HANDBOOK

☐ Present your information in a simple A5 leaflet, designed for someone new to working with elderly people at home in your area. Include contact names, addresses, phone numbers. Explain who is eligible to receive the services and how to make contact.

ACTIVITY 5:
CLOSER TO HOME

☐ Think about an elderly person you know in this structured way. It may be a relative, a neighbour or a person you care for.

(*a*) Draw a diagram showing their present contacts;

(*b*) Assess how these contacts could help the elderly person if they need help;

(*c*) Identify the additional services they need or might need in the near future.

Assignments

Assignment 1
Out and about in
the locality

TASK 1:
FINDING OUT

For this task you will need

- a blank large scale map of your area and a clipboard;
- access to phone books and other reference books giving addresses of local amenities and shops.

Your task is, with a partner, to find the following places and to mark them on the map. The first five also have a question to answer. **Before you go**, decide

- which places you will be able to find just by going out and looking
- which you need to look up first in a telephone directory or other directory
- how long to allow for the exercise and when to report back.

1 Public library: what are the opening hours?
2 Job Centre
3 Employment agency
  Is either of these above two places advertising a job you could apply for in a year's time? If so, note down details; post, hours, pay.
4 Citizens Advice Bureau or other advice centre: what are the opening hours?
5 Health centre or doctor's surgery: what are surgery times?
6 Town Hall/neighbourhood centre
7 Bank
8 Building society
9 Police Station
10 Supermarket
11 Chemist
12 Social Security Office
13 Park
14 Dentist
15 Social services office
16 Post Office
17 Meeting place eg Church Hall

Add

18 One place of interest to someone of your age;

19 One place you particularly liked;

20 One place that might be useful to someone you know.

**TASK 2:
OPEN ACCESS?**

Can everyone get around your area, in and out of buildings and shops as easily as you can?

1 Discuss the following points:
- Who might experience difficulty with access to shops and buildings in your area?
- Which specific features cause these difficulties?

You may like to start your discussion by considering how accessible your area would be to each of the people in the Case Studies.

2 With a partner, go to your local shops or shopping centre, and investigate how user-friendly it is to the groups of people you identified above. You will need a clipboard and a copy of the points below. Ensure that, between you, the group covers

(*a*) the places identified in Task 1, and

(*b*) a selection of shops for day-to-day shopping; supermarket, corner shop, newsagent, greengrocer, butcher, baker, and any others you think should be added.

User-friendly points

- Doors wide enough for prams and wheelchairs
- Aisles wide enough for prams/buggies and wheelchairs
- Ramps or doors without steps
- Supermarket trollies with seats for children
- Safe keeping for prams, pushchairs if they cannot be taken into the shop
- Baby changing/feeding areas
- Areas where children can play
- Supervised play
- Free delivery
- Free telephone to order taxi
- Telephone orders
- Special services such as clothes alteration
- Goods in small quantities
- Assistants who understand sign language
- Information in braille
- Disabled parking areas
- Convenient pedestrian crossings
- Information in different languages

3 Report back on your findings to the class. Plan your talk well in advance by:

(*a*) Making sure the title of your presentation reflects your investigation;

(*b*) Deciding on the points you want to make and a heading for each;

(*c*) Dividing your findings between the headings. For each point, provide an example to back up what you say; and

(*d*) Ending with a conclusion in which you make a judgement about how accessible your area is for *all* local people.

TASK 3:
MAKING CONTACT

For this task you need to refer to *either* the diagram showing the structure of a local authority (on p 23); *or* a copy of a diagram or information sheet showing the organisation of local authority services in your area.

Using your diagram of local authority services, decide which department you would contact in each of the situations below:

Situation 1

You have noticed that the pavement in your street is in very bad repair. Paving stones are broken and missing, and several elderly people have fallen and hurt themselves. Who do you contact for action?

Situation 2

A pile of rotting rubbish has built up around the corner. Bags have split open, more rubbish is now being dumped, and you have seen rats there. Who do you contact for action?

Situation 3

You are concerned that dogs get into the children's play area in the park through a hole in the fence and foul the area. You consider this to be a serious health hazard to young children. The attendant agrees, but says there is nothing she can do about it. Who do you contact for action?

Situation 4

You want to know which of the local primary schools have nursery classes attached to them. How do you find out? If you had a children of nursery age, would they be accepted by the school of your choice?

Situation 5

Some contractors working for the council rewired your council house last week. They sliced through tiles down the middle of the bathroom floor, and through a bedroom carpet in order to lift the floorboards. They were unhelpful when you complained – they said it could not be helped and left. Who do you contact for action?

TASK 4:
GETTING
SOMETHING DONE

Work with a partner in this task.
1   For each of the above situations, decide
     ● exactly **what action** you want the council to take
     ● the **best way** of going about getting the outcome you want
     When you have discussed it, record your notes under two headings, 'Desired Action/Outcome'; and 'Steps to Take' (e.g. 1 phone call, 2 letter, 3 visit)
2   **Role play.** Work through one of the situations. One person should take the

part of the person making the complaint, and the other should take the part of the official receiving the complaint. Work through the 'Steps' you decided upon above; if you decided on a phone call first, start your role play with a phone conversation; if you decided on a visit, role play a face-to-face complaint.

Can you suggest some 'do' and 'don't' tips for making a complaint?

3   Discussion: how to be effective. Report back to the whole group what you decided was the best way to go about getting a satisfactory outcome to your complaint.

**TASK 5:
WRITE A LETTER**

Write a letter to the appropriate department of the council about your complaint. Make sure you

- explain your concern;
- are clear about the action you want taken;
- use an appropriate tone and style; and
- set out the letter correctly.

For advice on letter layout, *see* p 276.

Assignment 2:
Getting to know local services

Many people doing a wide range of jobs are involved in providing the services for people who need care. The local authority and health authority already work together to refer people to each other's services, and as Part 1 of this book demonstrated, they will offer a more integrated service in the future.

Below are descriptions of some of the people involved in the caring services.

Catrin Jones is a level 2 social worker employed by the Social Services Department. She works with all sorts of people, dealing with a range of problems. 'My job', she says, 'is to enable individuals and families to manage their lives more easily and to give help in time to avoid serious breakdowns or crises. I try to work closely with other people in the caring services – GPs, housing workers, the DSS to name but a few'.

Catrin works as part of a social work team in a 'patch' – i.e. an area of the city, but soon, when the department is reorganised, she will join the specialist team working with the elderly. Clients are referred by GPs, health visitors and the probation service.

To become a social worker Catrin took a four-year CQSW course at her local polytechnic. Before this she had studied A levels at school and worked as a youth worker on an adventure playground.

Mildred Brown is a home help. She has been a home help for six years and has always worked part time. She meets the Home Help Organiser on a Monday morning and together they plan how Mildred's hours will be allocated.

'I visit elderly people in their homes and help them with the things they can't do any more. Some people see us as Mrs Mops but we do far more than just clean. Most old people love to see us; often we are the only people they see to talk to from one week to the next. Sometimes they get better, sometimes if they seem poorly we call in the district nurse or the doctor.'

Mildred became a home help after working as an ancillary nurse in a private home for elderly people. She is employed by the Social Services Department.

Errol Johnson is a Community Psychiatric Nurse helping people suffering from a mental illness to remain in the community and stay out of hospital.

'My job,' he says, 'is to follow up patients discharged from hospital to give them their medication or check that they are taking it. I am the link between the hospital and the world outside. I make sure they are getting on all right – sometimes I suggest things they can do or places to go to. They often need help with finding jobs and housing. If people have no work or are unhappy with where they are living, of course their chances of recovery are affected. To do this I work very closely with hospital staff and the Social Services.'

Errol trained for three years to become a Registered Mental Nurse and then worked for two years in a psychiatric ward of a general hospital before he became a CPN. He is employed by the Health Authority.

Doris McIntyre is a child-minder looking after pre-school children in her own home. She is registered with her local social services department who have given her permission to look after up to three children.

She says, 'I love children. Now my own are at school I love having the little ones in my home and I think it's better for the children to be looked after in a homely atmosphere. I have one little boy from 8.00 till 6.00. The baby's mum works three days a week, and Joanne comes in the mornings only. I love it and they all get on well.'

Doris has no academic qualifications but a great deal of experience from bringing up her own children. She has just started a PPA course (Pre-School Playgroups Association) which will give her a qualification. Doris sets her own fees in line with the social services scale of charges.

Paul Quinton is a GP who works in a group practice of five doctors. Like all GPs, they contract with the Family Health Services Authority (FHSA) to offer 'general medical services' to the people registered with them. People come to see them with all sorts of health problems, and they treat and prescribe where they can and refer patients to specialists when they think this is appropriate.

'The GP is the first port of call for people with all sorts of problems – not all of them strictly medical', he says. 'Everybody knows their GP – not everybody knows where to contact a social worker, or whether social workers can offer the help needed. So we do a lot of listening, to see what is really bothering people and refer them on if we can't help.

My practice aims to offer the full range of primary health care services, and look after the whole family. We all do home visits, surgeries, and a session in the local hospital. Sue, the practice nurse, treats people with minor illnesses, for example, children with ear-aches. She works in the family planning clinic but most of her time at present is taken up with health promotion. It means we can refer people to her for advice on smoking and diet, leaving us more time for medical conditions.

The District Nurse holds a dressings clinic in our practice and community midwives work with us in maternity services and ante-natal clinics. We hold well-baby clinics for child development tests and immunisations. We work closely with Samina Khan, the health visitor, and she does a lot of follow-up work.

We've had a lot of admin work to do this last year, but now our records are almost all computerised, we've found we are already meeting the government's targets for immunising children and cervical smears . . . . . .'

To get into medical school, you need three science 'A' levels with good grades. After five years as a medical student, Paul worked for three years in a hospital, one as a House Officer and two as a Senior House Officer gaining experience of different specialisms. After this, Paul decided to become a GP and applied for a three-year training scheme. This took him through two more years of hospital training doing pediatrics, maternity, geriatrics, casualty – specialisms directly relevant to a GP's work. Paul found his own training practice for the third year and, when one partner decided to go half time after she had a baby, he applied, successfully, to join the practice.

Samina Khan is a health visitor, employed by the District Health Authority. She works from a GP group practice (she works with Paul) so most of her clients are on the doctors' list, which makes it easier to contact mums at clinics and get in touch when a problem arises. The practice also accepts referrals from social workers or teachers and other professionals involved with pre-school children. Health visitors have a statutory responsibility to visit newborn babies, taking over from the midwife when the baby is ten days old. They then visit or phone periodically until the child reaches school age.

Samina says, 'My job is to help parents with their young children. I view my job from a very practical level. Most parents have worries at some point; if your baby cries a lot or seems in pain you need to know if there is anything wrong, and if not, what to do. I can't always solve the problem but it often helps just to know that it's quite normal! I give advice on feeding, practical care, and remind parents about immunisation and developmental tests. Parents often ask me about playgroups and nurseries – I help with this too.'

Before becoming a health visitor Samina trained for three years to become a Registered General Nurse. After working as an RGN for two years she went back to college for one year to study for the Health Visitor Certificate.

Jill Shaw is an adviser at a Citizens Advice Bureau which provides free, impartial, confidential advice and help to anybody on any subject.

'It is very interesting work and very worthwhile – but often hectic. On an average day I may give advice on anything from gluesniffing to eviction or a complaint about faulty goods. We have a lawyer in twice a week – this helps with the complicated cases, and we do refer people on for help from other agencies once we have worked out what the problem is about.'

The Citizens Advice Bureau is a voluntary organisation so Jill receives no payment for the work she does. Jill worked for the local council before she had her family. She started work at the CAB because she wanted to use her experience and help people; she has got so involved that she has gone on several courses to keep up to date with the changes in benefit and housing law. She is a mine of information about local voluntary organisations; she is in regular contact with the local branches of Mind, Mencap, PHAB, Age Concern, Gingerbread and housing associations and knows many of the people who work for them personally.

TASK 1:
THE CARE JIGSAW

The following questions could be used initially as the basis for a discussion, in which links with the background information given in Part 1 are made.

1   Which of the people described above work for
(*a*) the NHS
(*b*) a local authority
(*c*) a voluntary agency?
2   Which of these people do some **statutory** work?
3   What training for the job has each person had?
4   For which jobs is formal training not required? Look back to Part 1 and to the descriptions above to find examples of the sort of training that may be offered to people doing these jobs.
5   Which of the people might meet or contact each other in the course of a working week? In what context? What do you think are the benefits of training for these people?

TASK 2:
HELP!

When the people in the Case Studies in Part 2 want help, who could they go to? You may think of more than one person in each case.

1 Who could Angela Williams (*see* Case Study 1) talk to about her baby not sleeping at night?
2 Who could advise Angela about her benefits, and what to do about her mounting bills?
3 Who should Andrew Neale (*see* Case Study 2) contact initially to ask for a care attendant or home help to come and take over some tasks from his mother?
4 Who might he contact if he wanted to find out what disability pressure groups had branches locally?
5 Who would help Paul Weaver (*see* Case Study 3) decide whether he should return to hospital?

6 Who could help Paul Weaver look for a job? Who might this person contact to help?

7 Who would Gladys Miller (*see* Case Study 4) go to for her checks for diabetes, if she stopped going back to Netherdene for this?

8 Who would make the contact?

9 Who do you think will be the first person Liz Hill (*see* Case Study 5) contacts for help with her mother?

10 Which of the other people in the descriptions above might be able to help her and how?

11 In what ways could Mildred Brown help Mrs Taylor? (*see* Case Study 6) What skills would she require?

12 Which of these people might be the first to become aware of Mrs Taylor's difficulties? How might this contact be made?

**TASK 3:
FOR REAL**

Do you know anyone who does any of these jobs? If so, what personal qualities do they have?

Interview someone who does one of these jobs. Ask them about their training, what they do, the good and bad points about the job. Work out your questions or question areas first. This sort of open-ended interview would be ideal to record on tape – if they agree.

Assignment 3:
Clinic study

Part 1 of this book explained how the NHS works and the changes taking place within it. In this assignment you are asked to take a look at an aspect of primary health care at work in your area, by studying a clinic and the services offered there.

Your clinic study will have four parts:
1 **The location and layout of the clinic**
2 **The services offered**
3 **The people who work there**
4 **How it is organised.**

**TASK 1:
PLANNING**

1   Find out which clinics are held in your area. You will find clinics at:
   ● GPs surgeries;
   ● Health centres; and
   ● Hospital outpatients.
   For each, find out the basic information you need, for example: who the clinic is for; address, phone number and exact location; hours.

2   Work out a shortlist of four clinics which you would like to visit and which are willing to let you visit. Discuss with your tutor the best way to make contact to establish this – by phone? by letter?

3   Once you have agreement in principle to a visit, divide into four groups, one to study each clinic in depth.

4   Finalise the arrangements for your visit to your clinic.
   ● If you have to *telephone* think carefully what you are going to say; be able to suggest different days and times for your visit to fit in with their schedule.
   ● When you have agreed a visit, *write a letter* to confirm the details; date, time, purpose, how long you expect to be there, and who you will report to when you arrive.

**TASK 2:
PREPARING FOR
THE VISIT**

(*a*) Hold a classroom discussion on what you already know about the clinic and what you expect to see happening there.

(b) Decide who in your group will concentrate on each part of the investigation.

(c) Decide on the information you want to find out about the clinic in each part of your study. Some suggestions have been set out for you below.

Part 1: Location and layout

- Draw a map to show the clinic's location, or mark it on a large scale map;
- How do most clients get there? Bus? on foot? car?
- Draw a rough plan of the clinic, showing waiting areas, consultation/treatment rooms, reception/office areas, toilets etc.
- Does it feel well used by the community? Look out for 'What's On' notices, posters, play areas. Are health promotion messages and leaflets well displayed?
- Comments about general atmosphere and upkeep of the building

Part 2: The services offered

- Are several different clinic sessions held here? Draw up a timetable showing the days and times of the sessions through the week and who the services are for.
- What clinic is taking place today? What procedures are offered to the client at this clinic?
- Do staff follow up clinic sessions with home visits? In what circumstances?

Part 3: The people who work there

- List the jobs, and where possible the names, of the people who work at or from the clinic. What hours do they work?
- Which of these people are involved in direct patient care? What do they do?
- Which people offer support work? What jobs do they do?
- Do specialists come to the clinic to offer a particular service? What is this?

Part 4: How the clinic is organised

- How are appointments organised?
- Is there a computerised system for some check-ups?
- What letters or reminders are sent out?
- What is the system for linking the client to their records, before and after an appointment?

(d) Now design a 'Clinic Investigation Sheet', for your small group to complete on your visit.

(e) Decide who in your group will concentrate on each Part of the study

TASK 3:
THE INVESTIGATION

On your visit to the clinic fill in as much of your part of the Clinic Investigation Sheet as you can. You will need to

- look and listen
- ask questions

Remember! Be tactful and courteous. Do not ask questions when people are busy and ask permission before you wander around the clinic.

TASK 4:
REPORT BACK

(a) Meet up with the other people in your group to bring together the information you have collected. Plan your verbal report back to the rest of the group.

(*b*) Describe the work of the clinic you visited, and listen to the report backs of the other groups

(*c*) Write up your clinic study in your groups. You may wish to use a word processor to make it easier for you to contribute your part to the whole report.

TASK 5:
WHAT'S ON OFFER

As part of the current reforms to the NHS, the government is encouraging GPs and health centres to give more information to patients about the services they offer. Each practice has to produce a leaflet in which the services offered are set out.

Produce an A5 leaflet in which you describe the services and facilities of the clinic you studied. It should have the additional purpose of encouraging the right people to use the clinic. You will need to be selective about what you include to make it clear, easily readable, and useful.

TASK 6:
THANK YOU

Write and thank the clinic staff for helping with your investigation. You may also want to invite them to view your completed Clinic Study or enclose a copy of your leaflet.

Assignment 4:
The Well Baby clinic

Child health clinics or well-baby clinics are busy places, where parents bring their children for a number of reasons. They may have come for
- an appointment for an immunisation
- to see the health visitor for some advice
- for a developmental check
- to have their baby weighed and measured.

TASK 1:
WHY CHECK?

Whatever the parent has brought the child for, they are usually asked if they would like to have their baby weighed. Read the extract opposite and answer the questions that follow:

(*a*) Why is the weight and height of a baby checked so often?

(*b*) What is a centile chart? What do the heavy lines show? What do the lighter lines show?

(*c*) Does it matter if a child's weight goes up and down across the lines of the centile chart?

(*d*) Why do you think centile charts have spaces for marking in a premature child's weight?

(*e*) Give two examples of when you would suggest the mother talks to the health visitor.

Logging growth checks

Shown on p 84 are two growth charts, or **centile charts**, one for boys and one for girls. Boys are on average a little heavier and taller than girls and their growth patterns are slightly different.

Study the centile charts, and make sure you understand what they show and how they work. The thick line shows the weight gain of an average child, boy and girl, the 50th centile. The thin line above is the 90th centile – only 10% of babies are heavier than this. The thin line below is the

Growth

Weight/height checks

Checking growth, both in weight and height, is a simple way of checking a child's health and progress.

You can have your baby regularly weighed and measured at your child health clinic or doctor's baby clinic. Older children should be weighed and measured as part of other health checks.

At the clinic, your baby's growth will be recorded on **centile charts**. The lines already printed on the charts show roughly the kind of growth expected, in weight and in length. The middle, heavy line represents the national average.

Of course there is no reason why your baby should be 'average'. In fact, these centile charts were developed some time ago, using a white British population. As a result, the averages shown are not right for some ethnic groups. The average birth weights and heights in some groups is slightly different. Variations between ethnic groups need to be taken into account when using the charts.

It doesn't matter where your baby starts on the chart. Whatever weight and length your baby was at birth, there should be fairly steady growth, with a line curving in *roughly* the same way as the lines on the chart. During the first two years of life, it is quite usual for a baby's line to cross the lines on the chart. But if at anytime your baby's weight line suddenly goes up or drops (and it may drop, for example, because of illness), talk to your health visitor about it. Talk to your health visitor too if, after the age of two, your baby's height line does not follow a centile line or stops altogether.

Babies do vary in how fast they put on weight. What is looked for is not so much a steady week-by-week gain as a general gain over a period of time. For most babies, weight gain is quickest in the first six to nine months, and then slows. As a rough guide, most babies double their birthweight by six months and treble it by a year.

You may have a chart that is slightly different from the one pictured here but it works in the same way.

(Reproduced by kind permission of the Health Education Authority)

10th centile – only 10% of babies are lighter than this.

Centile charts used in clinics usually show length/height and often head size as well. These measurements are not taken routinely in the way that weight is, but a health visitor or doctor may take them to give a fuller picture of a child's development. Weight in relation to length/height takes into account a child's build so gives a better picture of whether a child is overweight or underweight than the weight alone.

It does not matter where a child starts on the chart; what matters is that there should be a fairly steady upwards curve like the lines in the chart. There is no such thing as an average child, so very few babies and children will follow the lines exactly – most children's charts will show little wiggles, with times of rapid growth and times of levelling off.

BOYS

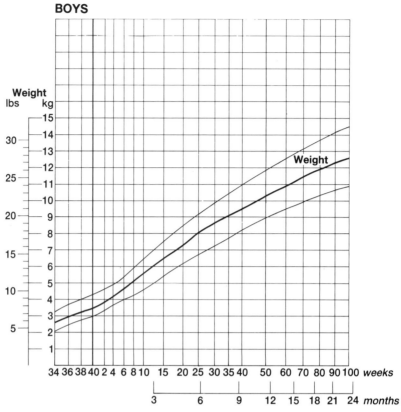

Centile chart: boys

GIRLS

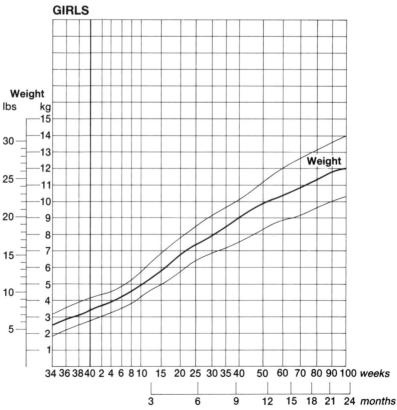

Centile chart: girls

TASK 2:
RECORDNG
CHILDREN'S WEIGHT

Using graph paper, copy out the two centile charts shown opposite, and record the weight of the six children described below. For each child mark each weight measurement with an x correctly on the right chart. Then join your xs to form a continuous line. Label each line with the name of the child. You may want to use a different coloured pen for each child.

Eleanor Rose: Weight at birth: 2.56k (5lbs 10ozs)

Age (in weeks /52 or months /12)	Weight (Kilos)	(lbs ozs)
2/52	3.270kg	7lbs 3ozs
4/52	3.75kg	8lbs 3ozs
6/52	4.36kg	9lbs 10ozs
10/52	5k 170gr	11lbs 6ozs
11/52	5.62kg	12lbs 6ozs
13/52	5.62kg	12lbs 6ozs

Grace: Weight at birth: 3k 460gm (7lbs 10ozs)

Age (in weeks /52 or months /12)	Weight (Kilos)	(lbs ozs)
4/52	4k 650gr	10lbs 4ozs
6/52	5.125kg	11lbs 4¾oz
4½/12	7k 750gr	17lbs 2oz
5½/12	8k 500gr	18lbs 12ozs
7½/12	9k	19lbs 13ozs
9/12	9k 850gr	21lbs 12ozs
1 year	10.400kg	22lbs 15ozs
16/12	11k 850gr	26lbs 2ozs

Jatinder: Weight at birth: 3.270kg (7lbs 3ozs)

Age (in weeks /52 or months /12)	Weight (Kilos)	(lbs ozs)
2/52	4.180kg	9lbs 3ozs
4/52	4.460kg	9lbs 14ozs
6/52	4k 800gr	10lbs 10ozs
2/12	5.420kg	11lbs 15ozs
10/52	6.280kg	13lbs 14ozs
17/52	6.480kg	14lbs 5ozs
4½/12	6.700kg	14lbs 12ozs
5½/12	7.2k	
7/12	8kg	17lbs 12ozs
8/12	8kg	17lbs 12ozs
10/12	8.850kg	19lbs 9ozs

Danny: Weight at birth: 2k 850gr (at 38 weeks pregnancy)

Age (in weeks /52 or months /12)	Weight (Kilos)	(lbs ozs)
2/52	3k 150gr	
4/52	3k 900gr	
6/52	4k 280gr	
10/52	4.950kg	
14/52	5.5kg	
4/12	6.150kg	
5/12	6.7kg	
6/12	7k 250gr	
8/12	7.6kg	
9/12	7k 900gr	
10/12	7k 950gr	
1 year	8.400gr	

Sharon: Weight at birth: 3.450kgs

Age (in weeks /52 or months/12)	Weight (Kilos) (lbs ozs)
4/52	4.125kg
8/52	4.950kg
12/52	5.350kg
20/52	7.100k
6/12	7k 900gr
8/12	8k 250gr

John: Weight at birth: 4k 200gm (9lbs 4ozs)

Date	Age (in weeks /52 or months /12)	Weight (Kilos)
1.6.90	2/52	5.050kg
16.6.90	4/52	5.875kg
30.6.90	6/52	6.275kg
23.7.90	10/52	6k 900gr
18.8.90	14/52	7k 450gr
16.9.90	4/12	8.100kg
19.10.90	5/12	8.675kg
19.11.90	6/12	9k 150gr
17.1.91	8/12	9.600kg
17.2.91	9/12	9k 850gr
23.3.91	10/12	9k 800gr
7.4.91	11/12	9k 800gr
15.4.91	11/12	9.950kg
29.4.91	11½/12	10k 100gr
10.6.91	13/12	10k 400gr
12.7.91	14/12	10k 500gr

Note: These are the records of real babies, taken from baby books. You can see that different people have done the weighing and record keeping. How do you write 5 kilos 620 grams? 5.62 Kg or 5K 620grs? And most parents still like to see weight in pounds and ounces, so you need to be familiar with these too.

TASK 3: MAKING SENSE OF DATA

You now need to make sense of these graphs, and think about the information they can give about a child.

1   (a) *Eleanor Rose*
    (i)   How old is Eleanor Rose?
    (ii) How close to average weight was she at birth?
    (iii) Do you think her weight gain is satisfactory?
  (b) *Grace*
    (i)   How close to average was Grace's birthweight?
    (ii) Has she developed steadily since then?
  (c) *Jatinder*
    (i)   How close to average was Jatinder's weight at birth?
    (ii) He was not well when he was 7½ months, with diarrhoea. Does this surprise you? Do you think there is any cause for concern?
  (d) *Danny*
    (i)   Comment on Danny's birthweight.
    (ii) Has he gained weight steadily?
    (iii) Is his weight gain satisfactory?
  (e) *Sharon*
    Comment on Sharon's pattern of weight gain.
  (f) *John*
    (i)   How does John's birthweight compare with the average?
    (ii) Describe his weight gain up to 6 months.

(iii) How often did John's mother take him to the clinic from 6 to 12 months? Why do you think this was?

2 If you worked at this clinic:

(*a*) Which babies would you draw to the attention of the health visitor in the clinic?

(*b*) Which parents would you want to encourage to bring their children to the clinic next week, or in two weeks' time?

(*c*) Which babies follow the pattern of the old rule of thumb; 'Double the birthweight by six months, and treble it by a year'?

Organising appointments at the clinic

Some parents at a child health clinic will be there for a quick informal chat with the health visitor. Most will probably have appointments for immunisations or developmental checks.

Health care workers and professionals generally involved in the clinics need to think carefully about the best ways of encouraging parents to bring their children to these important appointments, and to have systematic ways of following up parents when they do not turn up or can cancel.

Clinics have a number of ways of contacting parents to arrange appointments by:

- use of a 'baby book' which sets out the schedule of appointments and gives useful information
- making the next appointment as the parent leaves the clinic
- sending out post cards to give appointments
- sending out post cards when parents miss the first appointment
- phone calls and visits by the health visitor.

**TASK 4:
COME TO
THE CLINIC**

Below are some pages from a baby book, giving a schedule of the essential appointments for immunisations and developmental checks.

Immunisation – protect your child

Some dangerous illnesses can be avoided by immunisation. A course of protection against poliomyelitis, diphtheria, whooping cough, tetanus, measles and tuberculosis is important. We will send you information about where and when your child should be immunised. Remember, if you think your child has had measles it may still be important for them to have the injection for measles.

It is recommended that immunisations should not be given until 10 days after a child has finished a course of antibiotics.

If you have any questions or worries about immunisation please discuss them with your doctor or health visitor.

Recommended Immunisation Schedule	
Age	Immunisation
6 weeks	BCG (Tuberculosis)
3 Months	Diphtheria, Tetanus, Whooping Cough, Poliomyelitis 1st dose
5–7 Months	Diphtheria, Tetanus, Whooping Cough, Poliomyelitis 2nd dose
9 Months	Diphtheria, Tetanus, Whooping Cough, Poliomyelitis 3rd dose
15 Months	Measles, Mumps, Rubella (MMR)
4½ Years	Diphtheria, Tetanus, Poliomyelitis – booster

Developmental checks

Your child needs to have his or her development checked regularly.

AGE	CHECK	HEALTH WORKER	COMPLETED
6 weeks	developmental check	clinic doctor	
7–9 months	developmental check, hearing test	health visitor	
15–18 months	developmental check	clinic doctor	
2½–3 years	developmental check, hearing test	health visitor	
5–6 years	school medical	school nurse, school doctor	

You will be sent invitations to attend these checks.

(Taken from *Growing Up in City and Hackney,* published by the City and Hackney Health Authority, 1985).

(*a*) In small groups, plan how you think a clinic should remind parents to come for these visits, and follow up when they miss appointments.
(*b*) What will the next clinic appointment for developmental tests or immunisations be for each of the six children described on pp 85–6.
(*c*) Under the chart showing developmental checks, it says 'You will be sent invitations to attend these checks'. Draft a standard short letter or post card to send to parents to remind them to attend the clinic. Think carefully about wording; tone; language; and layout.
Make six copies of your letter or post card.
(*d*) Write to the parents of those children from the six listed on pp 85–6 who are due for an immunisation or developmental test within the next month to six weeks. Complete your standard letter or post card, to explain the purpose of the appointment.

TASK 5:
A 'BABY BOOK'

Design a 'Baby Book' for parents to keep. You must include the essential information on immunisation and developmental checks above, and a record of the child's clinic attendances. Consider which of these you would also want to include

- Birth information
- Health Services for your child
- Immunisation
- Development checks
- Health records and parents records
- Toys and play
- Infant feeding
- First aid
- Dental health
- Safety
- Hospital
- Useful numbers

When you have decided on what to include and on the number of pages, design and make up your book.

Assignment 5:
Clinic reception

In this assignment you are asked to carry out various tasks to gain an understanding of some of the skills involved in clerical duties in a health care setting.

TASK 1:
AT RECEPTION

Together with a partner, consider the following situations and decide on which solution you would choose.

(a) A client phones the clinic, asking for an appointment that afternoon. When you ask for the client's name you can't quite make out what they say. Do you
  (i)   write down what you think you heard?
  (ii) ask somebody else to speak to them?
  (iii) ask the client to repeat their name?
  (iv) leave a blank on the appointments form?

(b) A client becomes angry with you because they have had to wait a while to see the doctor. Do you
  (i)   explain calmly that the doctor will soon be available?
  (ii) phone through to the doctor and find out why he is taking so long?
  (iii) tell the person to calm down and wait like everybody else?
  (iv) tell the person that it has nothing to do with you?

(c) A client gives you his address but you are not sure how to spell the name of his road. Do you
  (i)   guess the spelling?
  (ii) ask the client to spell the word?
  (iii) leave the space blank on the appointment sheet?
  (iv) hand the appointment sheet over to the client and ask them to fill in their own address?

(d) A client comes into the clinic and asks you for some advice on the spots on his son's neck and arms. Do you
  (i)   have a look at the spots and suggest some medication?
  (ii) hand the client a leaflet on childhood illnesses?
  (iii) suggest that the client makes an appointment to see the doctor?
  (iv) say that you cannot help?

Self-certificate

SC1

And Sickness and Invalidity Benefit claim form

1 About you

PLEASE USE BLOCK LETTERS
If you cannot fill this form in yourself, ask someone else to do so and to sign it for you

Surname: Mr/Mrs/Miss/Ms

First names

Present address

Postcode

Date of birth

National Insurance number

CLOCK/STAFF/WORKS NUMBER

2 Details of sickness or injury

Give details of your sickness. Words like 'illness' or 'unwell' are not enough

Please say briefly why you are unfit for work

Tick one box

• Is your sickness due to an accident which happened while you were working for an employer?

   YES ☐   NO ☐

Tick one box

• Is your sickness due to a prescribed industrial disease caused by conditions at work, while you were working for an employer?

   YES ☐   NO ☐

NOTE: This does not apply if the accident or prescribed disease occurred while you were self-employed.

FORM SC1

3 Period of sickness

If you do not fill in this section or if you fill it in wrongly, it could lead to payment of any benefit you are due.

Everyone to fill in

Date you became unfit for work   day   19

Do not complete if you are unemployed

Date you last worked for any employer or as a self employed person   day   19

Time you finished work   time   am/pm

Night shift workers only

When did your last shift begin?   time   am/pm   day   19

Everyone to fill in

Do you expect to be unfit for work for more than 6 days not counting Sunday?   YES ☐   NO ☐
If you ticked 'YES', go to part 5

4 Returning to work

Last day of sickness before starting or seeking work   day   19

Date you intend to start or seek work for any employer or as a self employed person   day   19

Night shift workers only

Shift will begin at   time   am/pm   and end next day at   time   am/pm

5 If you are claiming Sickness or Invalidity Benefit

Go to part 6 'Your work' — do not sign below

If you are using this form for Statutory Sick Pay

Stop here. Sign below, and send this form to your employer

Signature   Date

Remember, if you are sick for a second week, your employer may want a sick note.

6 Your work

Tick one or more boxes

Are you?–

Employed ☐   Unemployed ☐   A student ☐

Self employed ☐   Other ☐

What is your usual job?

Please turn over the page

(Reproduced by kind permission of HMSO. Crown copyright 1989)

TASK 2:
OFF SICK

It is Monday. On his way out after seeing the doctor, Mr Bafitis shows you the form shown on p 91. The doctor has given him a prescription and told him to take the rest of the week off work.

He has picked up the form and asks you for help in filling it in. He tells you that he did his back in on Thursday on the morning shift (5am–12.30pm) lifting some heavy crates. He works for Garbo Storage Ltd as a warehouseman.

Self-certificate # SC1

And Sickness and Invalidity Benefit claim form

KEEP THESE NOTES

| Statutory sick pay |

- Only employed people can get Statutory Sick Pay (SSP).
  You can use this form for SSP if your employer wishes.

- To get SSP you must be sick for at least 4 days in a row counting Saturdays and Sundays.

- For SSP you only need to fill in sections 1-5 and send this form to your employer.

- There is more about SSP in leaflet NI244 available from your local Social Security office.

(a) Read the notes and write down what you would say in reply to the questions Mr Bafitis asks you;
  (i)   What is this SSP?
  (ii) Can I get it for sure?
  (iii) Do I have to fill in the whole form?
  (iv) What do I put in section 2?
(b) Now copy out and fill in the parts of the form which are relevant to Mr Bafitis.

TASK 3:
MAKING
APPOINTMENTS

Your task is to act as the receptionist at the Michelsham Health Centre, taking phone calls, seeing people as they go in and out, and answering queries. There are five doctors in the practice and one practice nurse, Sue Jamieson. Today, Tuesday, she

TIME	Dr. Laura Hopkins	Dr. Ben Seigel	Dr. Paul Quinton	Dr. Surpal Chutta	Dr. David Williams	CLINIC HEALTHY HEART Practice Nurse	TIME
9.00	Josephine Cooke	Mavis Johnson	Andrew Walker	Edith Palmer		Frank Haig	9.00
9.10	Mary Whalley	Moya Davies	Huw Evans	Emma Williams		Mr Da Silva	9.10
9.20	Shiela Hill		Ade Adeola	Koulla Demetriou		Hassan Djemal	9.20
9.30	Fred Winter	Andrew Onatoshu				May Dodd	9.30
9.40		Vera Phillips		Elsie Jones		Mr P. Cowper	9.40
9.50	Liam McAteer	Desmond Prospere	Costas Eperetos				9.50
10.00	Ken McLeish			Alan Rees		Fred Hall	10.00
10.10	Zee Khan	Richard Phelps		Gemma Braithwaite		Pat McLeith	10.10
10.20	Paul Harran	David Castri	Eddie Mason				10.20
10.30		Nishe Patel		Stan Packard		Kevin O'Shea	10.30
10.40	Stella Kumani	Mary O'Brian	Joe Little	Jimmy Chou			10.40
10.50		John Williams	Gary Blackwell				10.50
11.00	Phyllis Beckett		Stan Cohen				11.00
11.10		Kevin Baker					11.10
11.20							11.20
11.30							11.30
11.40							11.40
11.50							11.50
16.00			Philip Cryer	Daisy Mulligan			16.00
16.10	Hitesh Joshi		John Boxtans		Gianni Ferrari		16.10
16.20	Carl Wistfilla		Melanie Jones	Dean Hodgson	Kim Su		16.20
16.30							16.30
16.40	Daniela Bianchi			Wayne Moore			16.40
16.50	Matthew Johnson		Angus McBride	Sam Mandelbaum	Patty Martin		16.50
17.00	Nicky Chan		Anita Black				17.00
17.10			Steven Carpenter	R. Tat	Martin Patterson		17.10
17.20			Robbie Georgan	Steve Adede	Lech Spilberg		17.20
17.30			Nisha Patel				17.30
17.40	Arthur Fox		Kerry Nielson				17.40
17.50	Chris Coughlan		Sian Colwyn	Betty Sharpe	Huriyι Mehmet		17.50
18.00	Essan Faik			Tim Palmer	Josie Khan		18.00
18.10	Ester Kesselman						18.10
18.20							18.20
18.30							18.30
18.40							18.40
18.50							18.50
	Dr. Laura Hopkins	Dr. Ben Seigel	Dr. Paul Quinton	Dr. Surpal Chutta	Dr. David Williams	Practice Nurse	

holds a 'Healthy Heart' clinic, taking patients referred by the doctors. Surgeries are held 9–11am and 4–6pm. Appointments are made for ten minute slots, and sometimes for longer. People without appointments are fitted in where a doctor has gaps or are asked to wait to the end of surgery, so the last patient leaves quite a long time after the official end of surgery. In the middle of the day the doctors do home visits, admin, attend meetings etc, and most of them hold a session at the local hospital once a week.

(a) With a partner, take it in turns to be receptionist and patient, and decide what you would say to each of the enquiries listed below. Write down what you would say. Where you need to supply a name, invent one.

(b) Make appointments for those who require them and fill in the appointments page with the correct details.

- My name is Mrs McDonald, can I have an appointment for my son Jamie to see Dr Seigel this morning?
- I have an appointment with Dr Quinton at 4 o'clock this afternoon. Can I change it to 5 o'clock?
- I have an appointment for 11 o'clock with Dr Hopkin but is there any chance of my seeing her before 10?
- I would like to see a female doctor this morning. My name is Mrs Balachandran.
- Can I make an appointment for my mother, Mrs Akinsole, to see Dr Chutta early in the afternoon surgery?
- I missed my appointment yesterday. Can I have one for today? My name is Gary Stubbs.
- Is it possible to see a doctor in my lunch hour today?
- It's Sally Taylor. Can I have an appointment to see Dr Quinton this morning please? It's for Alice.
- I'd like to see a doctor today after work. What is the latest I can make an appointment for? My name is Dave Broene.
- My baby has coughed all through the night and I'm really worried. I'd like to see someone as soon as possible. Can you fit me in? My name is Michelle Williams.
- My name is Desmond Prospere. I know I've got an appointment for this morning but I've forgotten what time it is. Can you let me know what time I need to be there?
- Can I have an appointment to see Dr Williams today, preferably this morning?
- Dr Seigel told me to make an appointment for the Healthy Heart clinic. Is it too late to make one for this morning?
- I have an appointment with Dr Hopkin for 9.20 but I can't make it. Can I change it to after 5 this evening?
- I would like to see Dr Seigel today, preferably this evening.
- I've just seen Dr Hopkin – Ken McLeish – she told me to see the nurse at the heart clinic. Is there any chance of seeing her this morning?

TASK 4:
A FILING EXERCISE

(a) Copy out and complete Form FP95 (shown opposite) using your own details.

(b) Take it in turns to file the forms in order of

(i) age;

(ii) alphabetical order by surname; and

(iii) alphabetical order by first names.

Further practice in alphabetical order is shown in 'How to check alphabetical order on p 267.

National Health Service   **Form FP95 (Rev. April 1988)**

APPLICATION FOR CERTIFICATE OF PREPAYMENT OF PRESCRIPTION CHARGES

Please write names and addresses in BLOCK CAPITALS

Do not write anything in this space

Certificate No.

VALID from

to

(inclusive)

SURNAME	Mr.
	Mrs.
	Miss

FORENAMES
(underline the
MAIN forename)

FORMER OR ANY
OTHER SURNAME

DATE OF BIRTH

Day	Month	Year

Number of last certificate of prepayment
of prescription charges (if any)

No.

National Health Service Number
(as shown on medical card)

ADDRESS

PERMANENT ADDRESS
(if different from above)

PREVIOUS ADDRESS
(if changed since last medical card issued)

If recently arrived from abroad state date ....

If recently discharged from H.M. Forces state date ....

Your National Health Service   DOCTOR'S NAME
general practitioner   AND
(if none, write 'NONE')   ADDRESS

To the National Health Service Family Practitioner Committee:
    I enclose *Postal Order/*Cheque (made payable to
"HM Paymaster General" and crossed "Payee Only")

for *£13.50 in prepayment of prescription charges for *FOUR MONTHS   *(Delete unnecessary words)
    *£37.50   *TWELVE MONTHS

starting from (date) ....
    I have read and understood the notes overleaf.

    Signed.. Date...

(Reproduced by kind permission of HMSO. Crown copyright 1989)

Assignment 6:
As others see us

Are our attitudes the greatest handicap someone with a disability has to deal with? In this assignment you will be looking at attitudes – your own and other people's.

TASK 1:
GETTING ABOUT IN A WHEELCHAIR

For this task, each pair of students needs to use a wheelchair for a short while. You may be able to borrow wheelchairs from a hospital, School of Nursing, Health Centre, social services department, or volunteer bureau. Make these enquiries well in advance.

In pairs, decide who will sit in the wheelchair and who will push. Then go and carry out one of the errands below. In some cases, **the wheelchair user should be the person who is out shopping**; and the person pushing is simply helping their friend get around. In others, you are doing things together.

(a) *Errands*
   (i) Go to the Post Office. The wheelchair user wants to buy some stamps.
   (ii) Go to the library. Ask for forms so you can both join.
   (iii) Go to a fast-food shop and order a snack each.
   (iv) Go to a travel agent and ask about prices and times of ferry crossings to Boulogne. Find out if there will be problems of access for wheelchairs and if there are facilities for wheelchair users.
   (v) Go to a clothes shop and both of you choose some kind of top. Try it on if possible.
   (vi) Go into a bank. The wheelchair user wants to open an account.

(b) *Review*
   (i) Did you take a different route because of the wheelchair?
   (ii) Were the wheelchair user and the companion treated in the same way when you were both asking for or doing the same thing?
   (iii) Was the companion involved in decision-making on behalf of the wheelchair user?
   (iv) How did other shoppers react to the wheelchair user?
   Use these questions as the focus of your report back to the group.

(c) For the record

Write up your experiences. In your conclusion, describe how you felt during the exercise.

TASK 2:
STORIES BY
UNKNOWN WOMEN

Read the forewords to Stories by Unknown Women and Iris Cording's life history, and her story 'The Giraffe and the Tree'.

Discuss:

(a) What is the attitude of the tutors to the women who wrote the stories in the book?

(b) What impression do you get of the group members from their foreword?

(c) How did Iris Cording spend the years 1959–1979? How old was she?

(d) What is your impression of how she feels about her life since she left?

(e) Would you have thought that this sort of achievement was possible?

(f) Have you learnt anything about your attitudes to people with learning difficulties?

This book was written by the Parents' Workshop, run for women with learning difficulties at Islington Elfrida Rathbone.

Our aim was to help these women discover their own imagination and share it with their children. They illustrated their own stories with linoprints, stencils, embroidery, collage and drawing; when one medium didn't work we tried another.

A sense of achievement generated other activities: trips with the children, fundraising, setting up regular advisory visits from a child psychotherapist.

The group's success emerges in the originality of each woman's contribution, and points an alternative to more conventional measures of success.

BARBARA STEPHA, Literacy Tutor
JENNY SPRINCE, Recreation Worker

This group is mostly for mothers. We like the group, meeting everybody, talking with friends.

The people are very nice in the creche who look after the kids; their names are Beverly and John.

We've sent letters out to get funding. We are looking very much forward to seeing the book out on the market. We hope we can publish more books in the future and more women will come to the club.

We have enjoyed writing our stories and doing the pictures, so that other people know what we've been doing and can do the same. We shall show our friends and family.

GROUP MEMBERS

(Taken from Stories by Unknown Women. Reproduced by kind permission of Elfrida Rathbone Islington)

(Taken from *Stories by Unknown Women*. Reproduced by kind permission of Elfrida Rathbone Islington)

Iris Cording

I was born in Paddington in May 1945. I went to Paddington School until I ws thirteen. In 1959, when I was fourteen, I went to stay in St. Lawrence's Hospital, where I stayed until 1979. I slept there in a big room with lots of beds. I used to make the beds. I am married and I have twins. In 1985 I went on holiday to the Isle of Wight. It was a good holiday and I didn't want to come home. I like needlework and writing. I have enjoyed being married.

The Giraffe and the Tree

The giraffe lived at the zoo in a cage. He was asleep and dreaming. He wake up morning, eat food, meat and grass and water. Go out in field. He see a tree. He walked about, sit down, nice day, not raining. People say: "Not a dog, it's a giraffe, all spotty!" Giraffe thought all people stupid because not got long legs. He kicked all the people. The people ran away, get the zoo keeper to put giraffe in cage. The zoo keeper put rope over giraffe's neck, not tight, loose. Happy people. Giraffe go back the cage. Happy giraffe.

TASK 3:
THE LEGAL RIGHTS
OF PATIENTS

Read the article on p 100, about one aspect of the work of the Advice and Law Centre at Springfield Hospital in Wandsworth. The Centre is one of the very few located in a psychiatric hospital, and it offers patients advice and legal representation. Springfield was also the first psychiatric hospital in the country to have a branch of a high street bank on-site, providing services equally to patients and staff.

(a) Answer the following questions on the above article;

    (i)   Can staff find out how much money patients have in their accounts?

    (ii) If staff think a patient will spend their money unwisely, can they stop them taking money out of their accounts?

    (iii) What is the legal view of the capacity to make a decision?

    (iv) What is the difference between 'incapable' and 'incompetent'?

    (v) What happens to a patient's money if they are deemed 'incapable'?

(b) Do you think that patients should be allowed to have access to their money, even if they spend it unwisely? If so, why?

Legal ways to help patients balance their budgets

It is now three months since Lloyds Bank opened its doors at Springfield and Wendy Semp started helping patients with benefit claims.

A system has been introduced for patients which respects the confidentiality of a person's financial circumstances and gives control to the person whose money it is.

Patients can give authority to a third party to find out what money they have. Staff cannot find out, in order e.g. to plan a rehab programme, without the patient's consent and can no longer control someone's money, e.g. to prevent them giving it away, frittering it away or drinking it away.

If a patient is considered to be too ill to manage money, a decision has to be made about whether they have the mental capacity to manage their financial affairs and, if not, what is the most appropriate way of dealing with this.

Capacity

Generally, the law assumes that a person has the capacity to make a decision until they demonstrate otherwise. The law has never taken the approach that an individual is incapable of taking all decisions.

The test for incapacity relates to the particular decisions that have to be taken and the person's capacity at the time, e.g. the Income Support personal allowance of £8.70 per week is meant to cover the cost of cigarettes, sweets, newspapers and other small personal effects. Most people have the mental capacity to decide how to spend that money.

The test of incapacity is about being incapable, it is not about being incompetent in the sense of making foolish or unwise decisions. It requires that the incapacity is due to a mental disorder. Neither being incapable nor being mentally disordered is enough; the disorder must cause the incapacity. What is in a person's best interests according to professional advice may not be imposed by denying the person's capacity.

Safeguards

If it is decided that a person is incapable of managing their financial affairs, appropriate safeguards must be made to protect their interests. These may be the appointment of a Department of Social Security appointee, referring the matter to the Court of Protection, or making an Enduring Power of Attorney.

Implementing such action should be discussed with the Central Services Manager and decisions should be reviewed regularly. Guidance will be sent out in the New Year.

Jennifer Rogers
Springfield Advice and Law Centre

(Reproduced by kind permission of Springfield Hospital, Wandsworth)

Myths of ageing – a quiz

QUESTIONS

1 Approximately what percentage of the population is of pensionable age?
    13%   17%   23%

2 Between 1981 and 2001 the number of people aged 85 and over is expected to increase by:
    50%   61%   79%

3 What percentage of people of pensionable age live alone?
    15%   29%   78%

4 Over half of all people over 65 see one of their children more than once a week?
    True   False

5 In 1980, what percentage of people aged 65 and over had a long-standing illness which limited their activities?
    44%   55%   76%

6 What percentage of people over 65 live in hospitals and residential homes?
    3%   10%   14%

7 What percentage of people over 65 say they have never received a visit from a local authority social worker?
    25%   50%   78%

8 What percentage of people over 65 receive Meals on Wheels?
    3%   13%   23%

9 Almost half of all pensioners receive means tested benefits.
    True   False

10 What percentage of people over the age of 65 suffer from a type of dementia?
    5–7%   10–15%   0–25%

11 An individual can expect their intelligence to deteriorate with advancing age.
    True   False

12 How many people over 65 graduated from the Open University in 1985?
    20   100   150

13 The present generation of 60 year olds are mentally fitter and more able than previous generations.
    True   False

14 Older workers have less absenteeism than younger workers.
    True   False

15 What proportion of people over 65 consider their health in general to be good?
    21%   30%   37%

16 Older people, including those with active social lives, are much less likely than people under 60 to be victims of crime.
    True   False

17 How many people over 65 say they feel miserable much of the time?
    8%   20%   35%

18 People aged 65–74 are more likely than any other age group to be engaged in voluntary work.

    True   False

19 Older people who reduce their activity tend to be happier than those who remain active.

    True   False

20 What was the age of the oldest man to complete the 1987 Mars London Marathon?

    65   76   81

(Reproduced by kind permission of Age Concern Greater London)

TASK 4: GETTING OLDER

(a) Take a few minutes to write your own responses to these two questions
  (i) What does old age mean to you? Choose some words that describe old age.
  (ii) How old is old? When do you think you will call yourself old?
  When you have done this, pool your responses on a board or flipchart and discuss the questions with the whole group.

(b) How much do you know about getting older? On p 101 is a quiz devised by Age Concern.
  When you have completed it, check your answers with those of the rest of the group.

(c) Discuss the following points and then write up your conclusions:
  (i) Do you think any of your wrong answers were caused by negative stereotypes of age?
  (ii) Divide your page into two columns. In Column 1 list six stereotypes of old age. You may find your first thoughts in (a) above helpful here. In Column 2 identify the consequences for elderly people, for us as individuals, and for society as a whole of each of these stereotypes.

TASK 5: LIFE EVENT OR CRISIS?

People vary in what they find stressful, and in how they react to stress. It is generally recognised, however, that there are certain major life events that most people find stressful. Some of these are;

- starting and changing school
- leaving home
- moving home
- changing jobs
- unemployment
- change of partner or end of relationship
- having a child
- illness
- bereavement
- separation and isolation.

(a) Discussion points:
   (i) Do you want to add to this list of potentially stressful events? Or take any away?
   (ii) Rewrite your amended list in the order in which you personally have found, or think you would find, these events stressful.
   (iii) How do people cope? What did you find or think would be helpful at these times? What would happen without this?
(b) Consider the lives of each of the people in the six case studies in Part 2.
   (i) What major life events do you think they have experienced? Does it seem that their needs were adequately met?
   (ii) What major changes can you see ahead of them? What sort of support do you think they will need to meet the stress of this situation? Where do you think this support will come from?

   Work in six groups for this task, with each group taking one case study. Show your analysis on a large sheet of paper or flipchart, and present it to the other groups.

Assignment 7:
Lifestyle and health

This is a major assignment on which a substantial input on health education could be based.

Shown in the following pages are four 'health profiles' on **smoking; alcohol; diet;** and **exercise**.

Each profile has a

1 Health message to think about and discuss;

2 Health Check Activity to complete;

3 A section on health in Wandsworth: some results of the survey 'An Apple a Day . . . ? A study of lifestyles and health in Wandsworth' to interpret; and

4 Your survey: suggestions for starting points for your own survey into each health profile topic.

The tasks of this assignment are summarised below.

TASK 1:
HOW HEALTHY
AM I?

When you have worked through the Health Message and Health Check Activity sections of all four profiles, draw up a portfolio of your findings about your own lifestyle and health.

Your title is 'How healthy am I?'

TASK 2:
HEALTH
PROMOTION IN
WANDSWORTH

Write a report on what you think should be the priorities for health promotion in Wandsworth. Write

(a) Terms of reference: a short paragraph setting out this instruction;

(b) Findings: one paragraph summarising the essential points of each topic area;

(c) Conclusions: one paragraph in which you state how healthy you think the people of Wandsworth are;

You should write one paragraph in which you say what you think what health promotion in Wandsworth should concentrate on.

TASK 3:
YOUR SURVEY

Each profile ends with a 'Your survey' section. The whole group should plan this questionnaire and decide how to carry it out. You may decide to divide into groups and carry out four questionnaires or to pool the questions and carry out a single questionnaire covering all four topics with a larger sample. For advice on compiling questionnaires, *see* p 279 in the reference section.

(*a*) As a group you will need to consider

- what topics to include
- what questions to ask
- how many questions to ask
- the wording of the questions
- when to use open and closed questions
- where to include follow-up questions
  When you have decided on these, agree on typing, printing and copying the questionnaire.

(*b*) Agree a plan of action to ask the questions;

- How large a sample do you want?
- How many interviews should each person conduct?
- How will you ensure you get a spread of ages and lifestyles?
- Timescale – what deadlines will the group work to?

(*c*) When you have completed the questionnaires, you need to collate them, interpret the answers, write up and present your findings. You may want to use computer graphics, coloured wall charts or a mix of methods.

(*d*) Now you have done the work, decide who you are going to present them to.

TASK 4:
RESEARCH

With a partner, research the impact on health of one of the four profile topics; smoking, alcohol, diet and exercise. You may wish to focus on a particular group of people or consider the impact on health of another issue. Stress, dental care, check-ups and screening are also possible topics for research.

Make sure someone from the group covers each area. Then

(*a*) Decide where to go for information.

(*b*) Go and do your research. Keep copies of free information, and make notes from sources you cannot take with you.

TASK 5:
A TALK

Present your findings to your own or to another group in a talk. Make your presentation as vivid as possible with statistics, demonstrations, posters, fascinating or frightening facts.

TASK 6:
DESIGN A POSTER

Design and make a poster to put across a health message.

Your message may be one that emerged from your research, or from research by other members of the group. You may want to target your message at a particular group of people – for example, health care workers? young people? older people? mothers? – or to a wider audience.

Profile 1: Smoking

1 Health message

Smoking is the largest single preventable cause of illness and early death in this country. In **England** and **Wales**, smoking kills about 80 000 people each year, and puts more than 100 000 people in hospital.

In the Wandsworth Health District, the Health Education Council has estimated that about

- 270 men and 130 women die each year from heart disease, lung cancer, bronchitis and emphysema, solely because they smoke
- 440 men and 165 women are admitted to hospital because they smoke and need treatment for these diseases
- 12 500 bed-days are used each year in hospitals in the district because people smoke
- this costs the National Health Service £933 000 a year in this district alone

The source of these figures is The Big Kill, published for the Health Education Council and the British Medical Association by the North Western Regional Health Authority, 1985. Reproduced by kind permission of the Health Services Research Unit, University of Kent at Canterbury).

2 Health check activity

Smoking is an expensive habit. Ask a smoker how many cigarettes they smoke per day, then copy out and complete the chart below:

Number of cigarettes a day	Cost per day	Cost per week	Cost per year
	£	£	£

3 In Wandsworth

From the pie chart opposite:
(a) Roughly what proportion of adults in the district smoke at all?
(b) What proportion of adults in the district used to smoke, but have given up?
(c) What proportion of the adults in the district have never smoked?

From the bar chart opposite:
(a) What percentage of smokers smoke over ten cigarettes a day?
(b) Wandsworth has a population of 145 000. How many people in Wandsworth smoke over 10 cigarettes a day?
(c) What is the average number of cigarettes smoked each day by people who use them?

(Taken from *An Apple a Day . . . ?*, published by the Health Services Research Unit, University of Kent at Canterbury)

HOW MANY PEOPLE SMOKE?

We first asked the 1,605 people in the survey whether they smoked, and if so, how often. Here are their replies

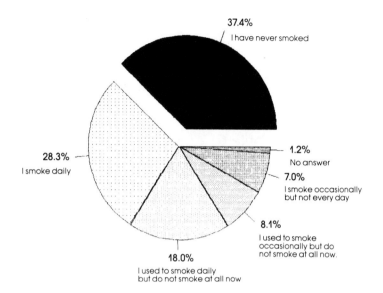

37.4%
I have never smoked

1.2%
No answer

7.0%
I smoke occasionally but not every day

8.1%
I used to smoke occasionally but do not smoke at all now.

18.0%
I used to smoke daily but do not smoke at all now

28.3%
I smoke daily

HOW MUCH DO PEOPLE SMOKE?

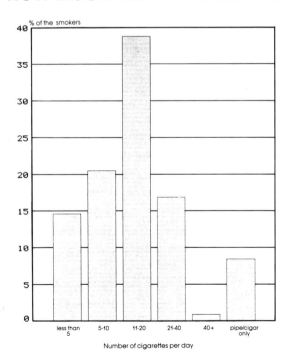

% of the smokers

Number of cigarettes per day

(Taken from *An Apple a Day . . . ?*, published by the Health Services Research Unit, University of Kent at Canterbury)

4 Your survey

In small groups or pairs, design a questionnaire on smoking in your area.

1   What question do you think were asked in the Wandsworth survey to produce the results in the two charts above? Start with these questions so you can compare your results.

2   Decide on the additional information you would like to find out about smoking habits and attitudes to smoking. Refer to Task 3 at the front of the assignment before you start.

Profile 2: Alcohol

1 Health message

The misuse of alcohol is a major preventable cause of illness, death and unhappiness. In Great Britain

- £15 000 000 000 is spent each year on alcohol – more than we spend on clothes and shoes, and half as much as we spend on food
- one million people suffer serious problems because of their drinking
- eight million working days are lost each year through people's drinking problems
- the cost to the nation of alcohol misuse is estimated to be between £1 500 000 000 and £200 000 000 each year

If the Wandsworth Health District is typical of the country as a whole, then alcohol is associated with approximately

- 65% of serious head injuries in the district
- 35% of road traffic deaths in the district
- 33% of divorces in the district
- 30% of domestic accidents in the district
- 30% of cases of child abuse in the district

(The source of these figures is an editorial in the British Medical Journal, 1985, volume 290, page 1. Reproduced by kind permission of the Health Services Research Unit, University of Kent at Canterbury.)

2 Health check activity

1   Read carefully 'What is a unit of alcohol?' Make sure you know the sizes of the glasses and measures described.

2   Ask five people to **estimate** how much alcohol they drink in a week. Ask people of different ages, sex, and lifestyles, if possible. Check what they say against

WHAT IS A UNIT OF ALCOHOL?

The rough guide here only applies to the drink you normally buy in pubs and licensed bars. Home measures tend to be more generous too, so take care.

There's the same amount of alcohol in a single whisky as there is in half-a-pint of beer or a glass of wine. And cider can be as strong or stronger than beer. Home brews could be much stronger.

Beware of those extra-strong brews, most are twice as strong as ordinary beers.

─────────────── **ONE UNIT** ───────────────

| 1 single pub measure of spirits | 1 small glass of sherry or fortified wine | 1 small glass of table wine | ¼ pint of stong lager, beer or cider | ½ pint of ordinary lager beer or cider |

Units (per week)		10	A sensible limit	Too much 20		30	Serious health damage	40		50		60
Women			14	22			36					
Men				21			35			50		

A sensible limit   Too much   Serious health damage

Drink ready reckoner

Drink diary

DAY	WHAT	WHERE / WHEN / WHO WITH	UNITS	TOTAL
MONDAY				
TUESDAY				
WEDNESDAY				
THURSDAY				
FRIDAY				
SATURDAY				
SUNDAY				
TOTAL FOR THE WEEK				

the 'drink ready reckoner' shown on p 109 and comment on their consumption.

3 Copy out and complete the detailed diary sheet yourself for one week and ask the five people to do the same. When you check it with them, be aware that drinks served at home are often more generous than the measures on which the unit chart is based.

3 In Wandsworth

(Taken from *An Apple a Day
. . . ?*, published by the Health
Services Research Unit,
University of Kent at
Canterbury)

HOW MANY PEOPLE DRINK?

We first asked the 1,605 people in the survey how often they drank alcohol. Here are their replies

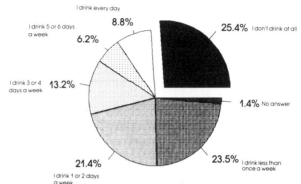

I drink every day
8.8%

I drink 5 or 6 days a week
6.2%

25.4% I don't drink at all

I drink 3 or 4 days a week 13.2%

1.4% No answer

21.4%
I drink 1 or 2 days a week

23.5% I drink less than once a week

1 (*a*) Roughly what proportion of adults say (i) they do not drink at all, and (ii) drink occasionally?

(*b*) What proportion would you say are light drinkers? Make clear what you consider to be 'light'

(*c*) What proportion do you think might be drinking too much for their health?

2 (*a*) Of those who drink, what percentage drink fewer than 11 units a week?

(*b*) From the information given in the 'drink ready reckoner' shown on page 109, what percentage appear to be drinking too much for health?

(*c*) Wandsworth has a population of 145 000. From the figures in this survey, how many people in Wandsworth would seem to be drinking a damaging amount (i.e. over 30 units)?

4 Your survey

In small groups or pairs, design a questionnaire on drinking habits in your area.

1 What questions do you think were asked to produce the results in the charts on p 112? Start with these so you can compare your results.

2 Decide on the additional information you would like to find out about people's drinking habits and attitudes to drinking. Work out the questions you would need to ask to find out this information. Refer to Task 3 at the front of this assignment before you start.

(Taken from *An Apple a Day ... ?*, published by the Health Services Research Unit, University of Kent at Canterbury)

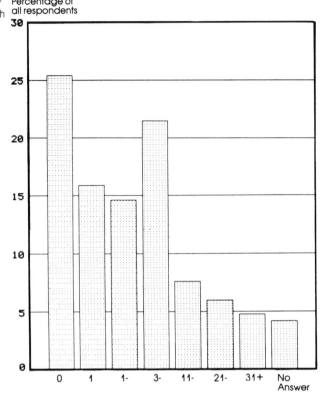

Percentage of all respondents

Average number of units per week

Profile 3: Diet

1 Health message

Healthy eating

**Here are some easy tips
about healthy eating:**

*Try grilling food instead
of frying it.*

Cut the fat off meat.

*Cut down on butter or use
a low-fat spread instead.*

*Use semi-skimmed or skimmed
milk instead of ordinary milk.*

*Use fish or chicken more often,
or the leaner cuts of red meat.*

*Try drinking tea or coffee
without sugar.*

*Go easy on cakes and biscuits
– try fruit instead.*

*Try to eat at least four slices
of bread a day.*

You can enjoy what you eat and protect yourself from illness at the same time. The wrong sort of diet, especially one with too much fatty food, makes your arteries more likely to clog up and makes you much more liable to a heart attack.

Eating well does not mean giving up all the things you like. It means eating a variety of foods, going easy on fat, sugar and salt, and eating more fibre-rich starchy foods like bread, pasta, rice and potatoes.

Ten tasty things you can eat more of:

Jacket Potatoes	**Beans on toast**
Chicken	**Pasta**
Fish or fish fingers	**Vegetables**
Fruit	**Rice**
Bread	**Liver**

(Taken from *A guide to Healthy Eating*, published by the Health Education Authority)

2 Health check activity

1 (*a*) Draw up a diary sheet similar to the drink diary on p 110 and keep a careful and honest record of what you eat and drink for a week. Make sure you include not only meals but snacks and drinks as well.

(*b*) Compare your record with the suggestions for healthy eating above and in 'Good Food' p 181.

2 (*a*) As a group, study the chart on p 114, giving suggested height and weight. Consider whether you think it offers good guidance for people of your age and sex. Take advice if you decide to recommend a narrower range.

(*b*) Ask five people their height and weight. Ask, if you can, people of different ages, sex and lifestyle and plot them on the chart. People are often sensitive about these details – so be tactful!

3 In Wandsworth

What people think about their diet

It is very difficult to get accurate information from people about their diets, and we made no attempt in this survey to find out what our respondents were

(Reproduced by kind permission of the Health Education Authority)

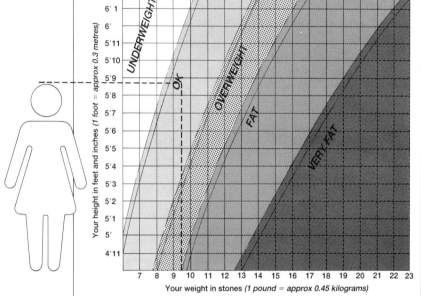

ARE YOU A HEALTHY WEIGHT?

Take a straight line across from your height (without shoes) and a line up from your weight (without clothes). Put a mark where the two lines meet.

Your height in feet and inches (1 foot = approx 0.3 metres)

UNDERWEIGHT · OK · OVERWEIGHT · FAT · VERY FAT

6'1, 6', 5'11, 5'10, 5'9, 5'8, 5'7, 5'6, 5'5, 5'4, 5'3, 5'2, 5'1, 5', 4'11

7 8 9 10 11 12 13 14 15 16 17 18 19 20 21 22 23
Your weight in stones (1 pound = approx 0.45 kilograms)

UNDERWEIGHT Maybe you need to eat a bit more. But go for well-balanced nutritious foods and don't just fill up on fatty and sugary foods. If you are *very* underweight, see your doctor about it.

OK You're eating the right *quantity* of food but you need to be sure that you're getting a healthy *balance* in your diet.

OVERWEIGHT You should try to lose weight.

FAT You need to lose weight.

VERY FAT You urgently need to lose weight. You would do well to see your doctor, who might refer you to a dietitian.

If you need to lose weight Aim to lose 1 or 2 pounds a week until you get down to the 'OK' range. Go for fibre-rich foods and cut down on fat, sugar and alcohol. You'll need to take regular exercise too.

actually eating. Instead, we asked them what they **thought** about their diets – whether they felt they ate too much, too little, or about the right amount of different kinds of foods. Illustrations were given of the foodstuffs in each category: for example, 'sugary foods', were listed as 'biscuits, confectionery, sweets, cakes, chocolate, fizzy drinks, etc'.

The following table shows the percentage of people in each of the three BMI* categories (underweight, normal weight and overweight) who thought they were eating **too much** of each kind of food.

(*BMI – Body Mass Index, weight (in kilograms) divided by height squared (in metres) – a way of calculating whether people are the correct weight.)

I THINK I EAT TOO MUCH . . .	PERCENTAGE OF PEOPLE IN EACH BMI CATEGORY WHO THOUGHT THEY ATE TOO MUCH OF EACH FOOD		
	Underweight	Normal weight	Overweight
fish	–	1%	2%
poultry	2%	3%	5%
lean meat	7%	7%	8%
processed meat	6%	2%	10%
sugary foods	27%	30%	37%
fried foods	13%	16%	18%
low-fat dairy foods	2%	2%	4%
vegetables and fruit	3%	3%	5%
high-fibre foods	1%	1%	3%
whole-meal bread	1%	2%	3%
salt	18%	21%	20%

(Taken from *An Apple a Day...?*, published by the Health Services Research Unit, University of Kent at Canterbury in collaboration with Wandsworth District Health Authority.)

(*a*) What proportion of each group think they eat too much sugary foods and fried foods?

(*b*) Do you think they are likely to be right in each case?

(*c*) Compare the foods about which people were questioned in the survey with the advice in the 'Healthy Eating' extract. Make two lists; List A of foods in the survey we are encouraged to eat **more** of; and List B of foods we are encourage to eat **less** of.

(*d*) What proportion of overweight people do not think they are eating too much of the foods in List B? What is the implication of this for health promotion?

4 Your survey

In small groups or pairs, design a questionnaire on eating habits in your area.

(*a*) If you decide to use the question in the Wandsworth survey, what information about each respondent do you need to find out?

(*b*) Decide on the additional information you would like to find out about people's diet and attitude to food and health. You will need to give careful thought to the questions to ask. Refer to Task 3 at the beginning of this assignment before you start.

Profile 4: Exercise

1 Health message

EXERCISE. WHY BOTHER?

■ Exercise helps you feel good in mind and body □ It's great fun, and a good way of making new friends and enjoying your leisure time more ■ It helps you feel more energetic ■ It helps you relax □ It helps you get slim and stay slim ■ It helps keep you supple, and more mobile as you get older ■ It helps strengthen your muscles, joints, and even your bones ■ It improves the staying power of your muscles □ It helps your heart work more efficiently, improves your circulation, and helps protect against heart disease ■ It helps almost everything in your body work better ■ It needn't cost anything ■ And it gets easier the more you do.

Four golden rules of exercise

Get moving

Use more effort than usual by finding a more active way to do the things you usually do, and by taking up completely new activities. Move through a wider range of movements and keep going for longer.

Build up gradually

It takes time to get fit. Work hard enough to make yourself a bit sweaty and out of breath, but not uncomfortably. That way there will also be less risk of sprains and strains. Always warm up first with a few gentle bends and stretches and cool down afterwards by walking slowly for a few minutes.

Exercise regularly

It'll take 20 or 30 minutes of exercise two or three times each week for you to get fit and stay fit.

Keep it up

You can't store fitness.

2 Health check activity

1 (*a*) How much exercise did you take in the last week? Include any exercise that made you puff.
(*b*) For the next week keep a daily record of the exercise you take.
2 (*a*) Take your blood pressure. How does it compare with the recommended range for a person of your age?
(*b*) Take and record your pulse rate in the classroom.
(*c*) Record your pulse rate after
- gentle exercise (e.g. walking to the next bus stop)
- moderate exercise (e.g. walking up an escalator, or long flight of stairs, gentle cycling)
- strenuous exercise (running for at least ten minutes, a vigorous sport)
Has this given you any indications about your fitness?

3 In Wandsworth

How much exercise do people take?

(Taken from *An Apple a Day . . . ?*, published by the Health Services Research Unit, University of Kent at Canterbury)

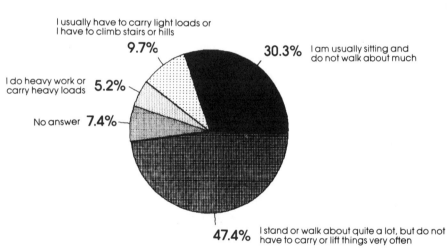

I usually have to carry light loads or I have to climb stairs or hills
9.7%

30.3% I am usually sitting and do not walk about much

I do heavy work or carry heavy loads **5.2%**

No answer **7.4%**

47.4% I stand or walk about quite a lot, but do not have to carry or lift things very often

1 (*a*) Roughly what proportion of adults spend much of the day sitting?
(*b*) What proportion spend much of the day on their feet, but not lifting or carrying anything?
(*c*) Approximately what proportion of adults do moderate or heavy work?

We asked the 1605 people in the survey whether, in the course of their normal daily routines, they were usually sitting for much of the time, standing or walking for most of the time, often carrying light loads or climbing stairs, or doing heavy work and carrying heavy loads. Here are their replies.

In round terms
- about half of the adults in the district spend much of the day on their feet, but not carrying or lifting things
- about a third of the adults in the district spend much of the day sitting
- and about a sixth of the adults in the district spend much of the day on moderate or heavy physical work

---

We also asked people how often in the previous two weeks they had undertaken vigorous sporting or recreational activities. The examples given of such activities were brisk walking, cycling, jogging, dancing, racquet or team sports, swimming and heavy gardening. Of the 1605 people in the survey:

- 60% said they had done no vigorous exercise at all
- 3% said they had exercised once
- 8% said they had exercise twice
- 3% said they had exercised three times

and 26% said they had exercised four or more times

(Reproduced by kind permission of the Health Services Research Unit, University of Kent at Canterbury.)

2 (*a*) Wandsworth has a population of 145 000. How many of these people had taken no vigorous exercise at all?
(*b*) Using the information in the health message section, how many people in Wandsworth are taking the recommended amount of exercise?

4 Your survey

In small groups or pairs, design a questionnaire to find out how much and what exercise people take, and whether they take enough vigorous exercise. You may like to start with the question asked in the Wandsworth survey, so as to compare your results.

Assignment 8:
Milestones in child development

At what age did you learn to pile up three bricks, walk and talk? The chances are, you do not know, and it really does not matter when you learned it; the fact is, you did. We all know that some people are better at doing certain things than others, and equally we can all think of particular things we do well.

To parents of young children however, it may seem as if their child is not developing as quickly as he or she should. Any parent will be anxious about some aspect of their child's development. 'Is it normal?' will be a spoken or unspoken concern to many parents. If you work with children, you will have a different perspective; you will see the great range of what is 'normal'. One child will be walking well at one; another crawling fast and confidently; another hardly moving at all. Yet they are all quite 'normal' stages of development for a one-year-old.

Thus, development can be seen in terms of 'milestones' – a point that is passed sooner or later. There *is* a range of 'normal' development; and sometimes everything is not all right. So people who work with children have to be sensitive to parents' worries and know when to encourage them to seek advice.

Where children do have a disability or special need, development in a particular area may be delayed. There are all sorts of causes for this; for example, impaired hearing may affect speech; a physical difficulty with movement will make many standard measurements of intellectual development meaningless. Children with special needs still develop, but milestones may be passed later – sometimes much later, when these successes are also a measurement of the achievement made by the child, the parents and caring services.

**TASK 1:
CHARTING THE
MILESTONES**

Shown on pp 120–1 are:
1 a guide to development; and
2 a development summary chart.

Your task is to copy the development summary chart opposite onto a large sheet of paper and complete it using the information from the guide below. Draw a bar showing the span of ages at which each development takes place, and write neatly in each bar. It will help the overall appearance if you plan roughly what goes where before you start detailed drawing.

A guide to development

This guide gives an idea of the age range within which most children gain certain skills. The ages given are averages. Lots of perfectly normal children gain one skill earlier, another later than average.

Movement

Most children:
☐ lift their heads by about 3 months.
☐ sit without support between 6 and 8 months. If your baby is not sitting unsupported by 9 months, talk to your health visitor or doctor.
☐ start *trying* to crawl around 6 months. Some crawl backwards before they crawl forwards. Crawling may really get going around 9 months. But some children learn to walk without ever crawling at all. Others are bottom-shufflers.
☐ pull themselves upright and stand, holding onto the furniture, between 6 and 10 months.
☐ walk alone between 10 and 16 months. If your child is not walking by 18 months, talk to your health visitor or doctor.
☐ learn to kick or throw a ball between 18 months and 2 years. Throwing sometimes takes longer than kicking.
☐ learn to pedal a trike between about 2 and 3 years.

Handling things

Most children:
☐ will reach out for objects between 3 and 5 months.
☐ can hold an object and will lift it up to suck it between 5 and 8 months. At first, babies can hold objects but not let go. At about 6 to 7 months, they learn to pass things from hand to hand, maybe via their mouths. They learn to let go of things (for example, to drop something, or give it to you) at about 9 to 10 months.
☐ use both their right and left hands, without preference, until about 3 years old.
☐ can feed themselves the sort of foods they can pick up and hold at about 10 months.
☐ begin to feed themselves, very messily, with a spoon sometime after 14 months.
☐ begin to take off easy clothes (like loose, short socks) from about 14 months.
☐ begin to be able to build bricks between 15 and 18 months. Large bricks are easiest to start with.
☐ enjoy scribbling with a crayon from about 18 months onwards.
☐ can draw what you can see is a person (with a face and maybe arms and legs) between 3 and 4 years old. Like much else, this depends a lot on how much practice and encouragement they get.

			MONTHS																																	YEARS			
Movement	Handling things	Seeing hearing and talking	1	2	3	4	5	6	7	8	9	10	11	12	13	14	15	16	17	18	19	20	21	22	23	24	27	30	33	36					1	2	3	4

Hearing and talking

Most children:
- □ are startled by sudden, loud noises from birth.
- □ make cooing noises from about 3 months.
- □ by 3 months will quieten to the sound of a parent's voice, and may turn towards the sound.
- □ by 6 months are making repetitive noises, like 'gagaga . . . ' and enjoy making more and more different sounds.
- □ start to use particular sounds for particular things between 10 and 14 months.
- □ say something like 'mama' and 'dada' to anyone from about 6 to 9 months and to their parents from 10 to 12 months.
- □ by 18 months, can say between 6 and 20 recognisable single words, but understand much more than they can say. They also start to use language in play – for example, when feeding a teddy or doll, or talking on a toy telephone.
- □ can put at least two words together by 2 years old, and can point to parts of their body.
- □ can talk well in sentences and chant rhymes and songs by 3 years old.
- □ by 3 years old are talking clearly enough to be understood by strangers. A few 3 year olds may still be difficult to understand. It is normal for a 2 year old to pronounce words wrongly.

Seeing

Babies can see from birth, but for a few months they can only focus on what is close to them. So to begin with, the other side of a room, for example, is a blur, but a face close in front of them is clear – and interesting. The distance they can see gradually increases.

Many babies squint at birth. If you still notice the squint after three to four months, you should ask your doctor about it.

Most children:
- □ begin to recognise their parents by 2 weeks, and start to smile at around 4 to 6 weeks
- □ in the first few weeks, especially like looking at faces. They will focus on a face close in front of them, and follow it. They prefer the face of a parent, or a known face, to a strange one.
- □ can follow a brightly coloured moving toy, held about 20cm/8ins away, by about 6 weeks.
- □ can see across a room by about 6 months.

(Taken from *Birth to Five*, published by the Health Education Authority, 1989)

TASK 2: SPECIAL NEEDS

(*a*) Find out about illnesses and conditions that result in children having a developmental delay and special needs in education.

(*b*) Research one of these conditions in greater depth. You may be able to visit a ward, school, unit or centre that specialises in help for these children.

(*c*) Write up your research. Below are some suggestions for headings. You may think of others.
- causes/symptoms
- treatment/therapy

- services to help
- experiences of individuals and families, effects on families.

**TASK 3:
A CHILD WITH
SPECIAL NEEDS**

To do this task you need to spend some time with a child with special needs.

(*a*) If the child is *under 5*, use your completed development summary chart as a basis for observing the child's development. Consider the child's development under the headings; Movement, Handling things, Seeing, hearing and talking. You may find it helpful to use a blank chart to mark in your child's development. If the child is *over 5*, you need to prepare for the visit by making sure you know what development you would expect to see in a child of that age.

(*b*) Talk to the child's parent or carer to find out what they are doing to help the child's development, and what developments are taking place.

(*c*) Write up and present your study in whatever way you think best conveys the difficulties and achievements of your special child.

Assignment 9:
What does a child do?

Children play because it is fun and they enjoy it. Children develop through play. Play gives them the opportunity to use skills they have learned and to develop new skills. It is through play that they learn about how things work, what they can do, how people behave and interrelate.

Children will find their own opportunities for learning and playing if they are given enough encouragement. Babies who have just learned to grasp things will suck their fingers, and reach out for things dangling in the pram. A toddler will 'wash up' endlessly, pouring water in and out of bottles and cups. As adults, we need to make sure that the opportunities for exploring and playing are there and sometimes to suggest new possibilities but our ideas of play are often more fixed than children's; we often think of play solely as something children do with 'toys'.

(Courtesy: Bridget Calvert)

TASK 1:
OBSERVATION

(*a*) Observe a child over a period of half an hour. Draw up an observation chart such as the one illustrated below, noting down every five minutes what the child is doing. You can do this task during a visit to a playgroup or nursery, or by observing your own or a friend's child at home. Leave the last column blank until you have finished.

Observation chart	What is s/he doing now?	What is s/he playing with?	Is s/he alone? With others? Who?	Is s/he quiet? Noisy? Talking?	Comments and review
Start					
After 5 mins					
After 10 mins					
After 15 mins					
After 20 mins					
After 25 mins					
After 30 mins					

(*b*) When you have finished, think back over the 30 minutes and in the column headed 'Comments and review', record which activities the child
- seemed to find most interesting
- seemed to find least interesting
- talked to you about

Add any other comments you wish to make.

TASK 2:
RECORDING

(*a*) Make a rough estimate of how many minutes in the given half-hour the child spent:
  1 playing alone with 'proper' toys
  2 playing alone with things from around the house
  3 with you or other adults
  4 'doing nothing'
  5 playing with other children
  6 doing anything else (say what)

(*b*) Copy and complete the pie chart below to show how much time your child spent doing each of these things.

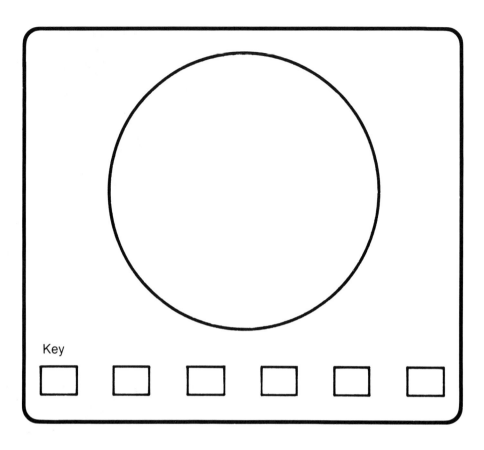

Key

**TASK 3:
COMPARE AND
CONTRAST**

(*a*) Compare your findings with those of other members of your group. What does this exercise show you about how children spend their time? Does any finding surprise you?
(*b*) Write a short report on what you and the group have discovered.

**TASK 4:
PRODUCTIVE
PLAYTIME**

It is not always easy to see a child's activities as an important part of the learning process. Sometimes it isn't, of course, and two year olds get up to mischief – perhaps just to see what you will do about it. But it is not all mischief or tiredness, sometimes a child's attempts at play will look like naughtiness to a parent or carer.

Joe is 2. Listed below are some moments in his day. Discuss how you would deal with each situation.

1 You are trying to show Joe how to build a tower of bricks. Whenever you get to five or six bricks, he knocks the tower down.
● What is Joe interested in?
● What do you say?
● How do you play together without either of you getting cross?
2 Joe is building. He gets four bricks piled up. He always positions the fifth wrongly and it all falls down. He is getting frustrated – and so are you.
● How do you prevent it ending in tears?

(Taken from *Birth to Five*, published by the Health Education Authority)

3   Joe loves standing at the sink on a chair messing about with water. He has been pouring water from a milk bottle to a cup, and down the draining board. He turns and pours a cupful on the floor.

● Is Joe being naughty? What do you say?

4   Joe is learning to use the potty. He knows what to do, but today, he stood still and weed, then said, 'Wee wee'.

● You feel like saying 'Naughty boy'. What could you say instead?

5   You come into the kitchen, just before breakfast and find Joe poking around in the cupboard. He gives you a cheeky grin and says, 'bic bic' (biscuit).

● What do you do?

TASK 5:
FILLING THE DAY

Study the pictures in 'Filling the day' shown on p 127. Discuss what is happening in each.

(a) Which of these suggestions do you think Angela Williams (*see* Case Study 1) might find helpful with

(i) Michelle

(ii) Ricky

When you make your suggestions, you need to take into account the ages of the children, cost of activities, amount of preparation, dealing with two children at once.

(b) Present your suggestions under the title 'Have a good day'.

Assignment 10:
Playthings

The observation for this assignment can be done at a nursery or playgroup, or at home observing a child you know.

(Courtesy: Bridget Calvert)

TASK 1:
TOY OR
PLAYTHING?

Notice two things a particular child plays with. They may be 'proper toys' or bits and pieces she or he has found or 'activity' things such as playdough, roller skates, felt tip pens, scissors or a bike.

Try and work out why the child enjoys playing with or using these things. For each note down the following;
  (a) What is it? Give a brief description if needed.
  (b) Is there a particular way it is supposed to be used? If so, describe it.
  (c) Does the child use it in other ways? If so, how?

TASK 2:
WHAT MAKES A
GOOD PLAYTHING?

The diagram below shows the main areas of development in a child.
1 (a) In pairs, use the diagram to consider the possibilities for play of each plaything you observed in Task 1. Write the item in the middle of the page. Draw lines out to the headings in the diagram and note down the ways in which this sort of play can contribute to the child's development in each area.
  (b) Present your diagrams to the group.
2 Discuss what makes a good plaything.

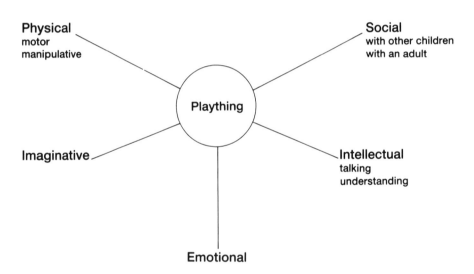

Areas of development
through play

Physical
motor
manipulative

Social
with other children
with an adult

Plaything

Imaginative

Intellectual
talking
understanding

Emotional

TASK 3:
DIFFERENT CHILDREN

(a) See if there is another person in the group studying a child of a similar age. Compare your child's favourite playthings with those of this other child.
  • What are the similarities?
  • What are the differences?
(b) Write a short piece (about half a page) about these similarities and differences.

TASK 4:
SPECIAL CHILDREN

Children with special needs need to play for the same reasons as other children. Where these children are different is that play for them is especially important. Children who have problems with mobility will not be able to find their own opportunities for play to the same extent, so opportunities must be brought to them, and the children helped to do what comes easily to others.

(*a*) Consider the play needs of the child you studied in Assignment 8. Identify two playthings that might help this child. You may choose something you saw when you visited the child, or something in common use with other children. Assess each plaything.

(*b*) Draw the diagram opposite to show how each plaything can contribute to the child's learning in each area of development.

TASK 5:
ANY IDEAS?

(*a*) Suggest a good plaything for a child in each of the age groups shown in the table below. Give a brief description (if necessary), reasons for your choice and its price, if applicable.

Age	Item & description (if necessary)	Reasons for your choice	Price (if applicable)
1			
2			
3			
4			
5			

(*b*) Compare your suggestions with those of other people in the group. Draw up a list of suggestions for each age group you all agree on.

(*c*) Do you think your suggestions would be helpful to Angela Williams (*see* Case Study 1) for Christmas presents for her children?

Assignment 11:
Toys

Read the two extracts about toys and play, entitled *One year to 18 months* and *18 months to two years* and answer the questions that follow.

Extract 1: *One year to 18 months*

Toy suggestions

Toys around the house   Present a young child with a large expensive toy dog that barks, and an old saucepan with a lid and a wooden spoon. Don't be surprised if the kitchen utensils are preferred. Why? Because they are simple, easy to play with, and you can do a lot of different things with them, like rolling the lid, filling the pan with bricks, and banging the spoon on the lid.

Bath toys   These can also be found in the kitchen: plastic measuring cups and jugs, and colanders provide endless amusement in the bath. Plastic floats and utensils can be used as boats as well as for pouring water.

Pushing toys   Trucks or laundry baskets which can be pushed are better than toys which need pulling: these make a child look backwards and therefore more liable to bump into things.

Wooden animals on wheels   These can be pushed along.

Boats   They can be floated in the bath or in a plastic washing-up bowl.

Soft toy engine or car   These can be sat on, pushed and used for imaginative play.

Picture books   Children may prefer those with few or no words, to be looked at with someone who will talk about the pictures, name the objects, and perhaps make up a story about them.

Extract 2: *18 months to two years*

At this age babies are usually able to toddle round alone. Their world is becoming bigger still. They are beginning to reason things out for themselves and to work out what will be the result of a certain action. For example, a little girl may squeeze a plastic duck and as a result of this particular action the toy duck will squeak; so she squeezes it again and again and laughs because it makes her happy. She then finds that if she puts it in her bath water it floats, and when she pushes it under the water it bobs up to the surface. Lots of messages have been passed at high speed to and from the brain, hands and fingers to produce these actions.

Now that they have started to work things out for themselves, toddlers like to push trucks along and watch the wheels go round. They may discover that if it is on a slope the truck will run downhill without being pushed. Gradually their games will become a little more complicated. At this age they like to pile one brick on top of another to build a tall tower. In order to do this they must be able to pick up and hold each brick in the hand, and then balance it on top of the last brick: the motor skills are improving. After carefully building the tower the fun is knocking it down, either with the hands or by pushing the truck into it. Towards the end of the second year, children begin to persevere more and finish the task they have started. For example, when playing with wooden pegs and a board, instead of putting in a few and then taking them out, they will continue to put them into the board until all the pegs have been used. They can pick up and use smaller objects now, little pegs instead of large bricks. If they are still putting everything in their mouths it is better to give them larger bricks instead of swallowable pegs. As they become more active they begin to climb on to chairs and, if these are not in the right place, for example to see out of the window or to reach that knife, they can easily push the chairs into the right place. The safety note here is obvious!

As well as becoming more active and being able to think about and follow through more actions, children may by now have acquired a few words. The same few words will be used for a variety of objects, but that does not matter because they are beginning to realize that using the right words will help them to get what they want. They will still point to things until talking becomes easier and their vocabulary increases.

(Taken from: Growing Up With Toys by Doreen Chetwood, published by Heinemann. Reproduced by kind permission of Doreen Chetwood).

1 **Extract 1:** *One year to 18 months*
   (*a*) Does the author think a young child will prefer a toy dog that barks or kitchen utensils to play with? Explain why.
   (*b*) Give three examples of toys for use in water suggested in the passage.
   (*c*) Why are toys that can be pushed better than toys that are pulled? Give three examples of toys for pushing.
   (*d*) What sort of books does the author recommend for use with young children? How might an adult use these books with a child?
2 **Extract 2:** *18 months to two years*
   (*a*) What mental development is beginning to take place at this age?
   (*b*) Why does the child find playing with the duck interesting?

(c) What changes take place in the play of a child who is nearly two?

(d) The author points out some possible dangers. What are they?

(e) How do children use their early words?

(f) Explain in a word or phrase what is meant by:

- reason
- high speed
- motor skills
- persevere

3   (a) Which ideas in these two extracts do you particularly agree with? Explain to the group why you agree with these ideas, drawing examples from your own experience.

(b) Are there any ideas which you disagree with? Explain to the group why you disagree with those ideas, drawing examples from your own experience.

TASK 2:
WRITE A REPORT

Think back on the ideas about toys and playthings in the two extracts. Look back at the suggestions you and the group made for playthings for children aged one to two in Assignment 10.

Now write a report entitled 'Toys for toddlers'.

TASK 3:
MAKE A TOY

Children love toys that are made specially for them. It's fun for the adult too. Often the simplest ideas give both of you the greatest pleasure. But simple must not mean dangerous, however well intentioned.

1   Before you make a toy for a child, read RoSPA's guidelines;

(a) Why is it important to know about child development before you make a toy?

(b) Why do you think RoSPA suggests you look at safety labels on toys?

(c) Give an example of a 'non-pliable facial feature' that might be used in a toy.

(d) How large would the smallest component have to be so as not to be dangerous to a small child that puts things in its mouth?

2   With this advice in mind, design and make your toy.

3   When you have finished, write a 'product label' for your toy. It should give information and advice on

- the age of child the toy is designed for;
- the learning it stimulates;
- how to use, treat and maintain it.

(Reproduced by kind permission of RoSPA)

Designing children's toys

Many of you choose to make a child's toy as part of a design project for an examination course. We cannot tell you how to design and make the toy but we can provide you with a set of guidelines.

Your guidelines

★ There are an estimated 50,000 accidents in U.K. homes each year involving toys, other playthings and sports equipment. You wouldn't want your toy to add to those figures, so 'SAFETY' is your key word. It is probably better, therefore, to make something that is relatively simple.

★ How old will the child be that uses your toy? Find out about the development and needs of children of that age. What are they likely to do with the toy? For example; a child up to two years may put everything and anything in its mouth. You may choose to make soft toys, bath toys or mobiles — things that are safe for such a child.

★ Look at existing toys for your chosen age group. Take note of any 'safety labels' or instruction/warning labels attached to the toys. Toys made to British Standards are preferable.

★ **DO NOT USE** — toxic paint, fragile or flammable materials. **AVOID** — sharp edges and points. **PLEASE MAKE SURE** — that any stuffing materials are clean; that ends of nails and screws, if used, are not accessible to the child; that non-pliable facial features are securely attached; that no toy component could block a child's windpipe if swallowed.

Assignment 12: Children's drawings

There are two tasks in this assignment, designed to organise your thoughts and observations on the drawings by children on the following pages into a single piece of written work – i.e. an essay.

There are a number of possibilities for **follow-up** work, which could come under the heading 'A child's view' and could include:

- studying a particular child and their drawings;
- studying the drawings of a sick child;
- showing feelings – what do playworkers in hospital or nursery workers learn about children in their care from their drawings?

These examples give an idea of the way in which young children's drawings of people develop as they grow older. But, of course children do not all develop at the same rate so their drawings will not fit exactly with the examples shown in this assignment.

TASK 1: DEVELOPMENT IN DRAWINGS

1 Look carefully at the children's drawings of 'a person' on the following pages. The drawings are grouped according to the ages of the children who drew them.

Take time, as a group, to discuss what you think they show about children's development, **how** children see people and **why** you think they see people in this way.

2 Write a paragraph, with a heading, on the first set of drawings, by children aged three. The main points to include are given as notes below. Rewrite the notes, using full sentences. Add your own comments.

General description
Many drawings have head only – simple circle – little detail – eyes clearly shown – nose and mouth usually shown – no body – legs attached to head – one shows feet

A particular drawing
Interesting head (third along, top row – how is it different?)

Your comments
Young child very interested in faces – especially eyes (why?) – bodies not important – legs next to be noticed (why?)

(Taken from *Children's Drawings, Children's Minds*, Rhoda Kellogg (Avon Books))

Drawings by children aged three

Drawings by children aged four

Drawings by children aged five

Drawings by children aged six

Drawings by children aged seven

Drawings by children aged eight

**TASK 2:
CONCLUSIONS**

(a) Now write a paragraph, with a heading, on *each* of the sets of drawings. You may like to follow the plan below.

General description
What do the drawings show – the whole body or parts? Which parts? How much detail is there?
A particular drawing
Does any drawing interest you especially? Explain why.
Your comments
What do you think the drawings show about how the child sees and thinks about people?

(b) When you have finished your paragraphs, you are ready to write your last section or conclusion. In this, describe the changes in how children see and draw people from the age of three to eight.

When you have finished, reread your work and correct any mistakes you spot. Give the whole piece a title.

Assignment 13:
At risk?

This assignment follows on from Case Study 1, Angela Williams. Before you start, re-read this case study and remind yourself of the difficulties the family faces. Ask yourself which problems you think might become more acute in the future.

This assignment has two parts:
Part 1 Building up a picture, a whole group activity; Part 2 Looking for support.

NOTE TO TUTORS: Part 1 is an exercise in teamwork. At each stage students will gain more information, and a fuller picture of Angela's situation will emerge – but only if the students share information as suggested. You will need to think through the organisation of this activity carefully and agree time limits for each part.

Practicalities: Books should be closed for Part 1. Copy out the points listed on pp 142–5 and make up individual cards of each point. Distribute them to the group as suggested below, giving out the cards in the order in which they are presented, as the information is structured.

Part 1: Building up a picture

You will be given fragments of information about Angela and her children; your task is to piece together the jigsaw of information to build up a full and accurate picture of life in this family. The question you have to reach a conclusion about is **whether you think either of Angela's children are at risk of abuse or neglect.**

Nine months have passed since the situation described in the Case Study.

Stage 1: First impressions

1   Sit in groups of three or four. Your tutor will hand you each a card. Read it and think about it. Tell the other members of your group what it says and comment about how it fits in with what you know about Angela Williams from the case study.

2   On the basis of the information you have as a group, decide on your response to the question – whether you think either of Angela's children are at risk. When you have decided, explain your views to the other groups and give your reasons.

Stage 2: Finding out more

1   Return to your small groups. Discuss the information you have learnt from the other groups. In what ways does this add to your overall picture? Has it changed your views at all?

2   Your tutor will give you each another card. Again, read it and think about what this information adds to your picture of Angela and her children. Explain your reactions to the other members of your small group.

3   As a group, consider again the question: 'Do you think either of Angela's children are at risk?' Share the view of your group with the other groups.

(Repeat this until all the cards have been distributed and used by the groups)

Stage 3: The full picture

As a whole group, decide, on the basis of the evidence you have, your decision on the question of whether the children are at risk of abuse or neglect.

You must reach a decision the whole group can accept.

The cards

- Mrs Blake, an elderly woman in the flat next door says she hears the children crying, and adults shouting at them, sometimes late at night.
- Ricky goes to nursery in the afternoons 1.30–3.30.
- Angela did not take Michelle to the clinic for her 15-month MMR immunisation.
- Angela has not been well recently. She has had a cough and cold off and on for about three months.
- Ricky does not like to share toys with other children in the nursery.
- Angela is in arrears with her electricity bill. She is being threatened with disconnection.
- Ricky is often eating a packet of crisps when he arrives at the nursery at 1.30.

- Ten days ago the nursery nurse noticed that Michelle had a nasty bruise on her forehead, and a graze on her nose. She only noticed because she heard her wimpering when Angela left her outside in the buggy. She had pulled her hat off.
- Mrs Blake, the elderly neighbour, reckons Angela goes out and leaves the kids alone in the flat. She went out on her own at 3.20 pm and came back with Ricky at 3.45 pm. She heard the baby crying while she was out.
- Angela did not go to the clinic for Michelle's immunisation (DPT) when she was nine months old.
- Ricky wet himself at the nursery the other day. Ricky seemed frightened. Two members of staff heard Angela shouting at him as they left 'Wait till I get you home . . . . naughty . . . . . your age . . . . . '
- She was sent a card from the clinic near her mum's she used to take Ricky to, reminding her about Michelle's 15 month immunisation.
- Des sometimes comes round late at night with a couple of mates. They drink and play loud music.
- Janice, who lives in the same block, also has a child – her youngest, Daniel – at the same nursery as Ricky.
- Angela is in arrears with her rent. They are deducting it from her social security. She finds it very hard to find enough for essentials like good food.
- A couple of weeks ago Michelle fell off the merry-go-round in the playground. Angela had looked round to see where Ricky was. Fortunately, she landed on the safety surface, so she only bruised her head and grazed her nose.
- Des sometimes collects Ricky from the nursery on Tuesdays.
- Samina Khan, the Health Visitor from the Michelsham Health Centre round the corner, has never actually met Angela. Notes about her have gone to and fro between the Michelsham Health Centre and a clinic on the other side of town, and she has only just realised that no-one has been regularly in touch. She realises that Angela has been living in the area for quite a time now and she is anxious to make contact. She has called twice, but Angela has not been in.
- Angela goes round to her mum's sometimes on Sundays. They all have lunch there.
- Angela has kept up payments on a settee Des bought.
- Samina Khan, the health visitor, called a third time at 2.00 pm. Angela was in, reading a magazine on the settee, drinking a cup of tea, smoking a cigarette. She said Michelle was asleep. She was not very welcoming. Samina told Angela about the Michelsham Centre and talked to her about immunisations. Angela seemed surprised there was a clinic so near. Samina did not stay long.
- Angela and Mrs Blake, the elderly neighbour, do not get on. Mrs Blake will not let Ricky play on the wide landing. She said her kids never could, so why should Angela's?
- Angela thinks she should give her kids better food. She tried a recipe from a magazine but could not afford half the ingredients. It was

horrible. Ricky threw it on the floor. She smacked him hard.

- Angela brought Michelle to the clinic near her mum's for her 15 month immunisation. She did not want her weighed and said she was in a hurry to collect Ricky from nursery at 3.30.
- Two weeks ago Angela told the nursery staff that Des would pick Ricky up. He did not come. Mrs Bessamy stayed with Ricky at the nursery and a helper knocked at Angela's door at 4.45. She was furious at having to collect him and swore at Mrs Bessamy.
- Ricky has twice bitten a helper at the nursery.
- Angela left the flat one night when Des and his friend came round. She could not stand them. Ricky was still up, but Michelle had gone to bed. When she came back she found Michelle screaming. She thought Des had yelled at her – maybe worse.
- Angela's mum thinks the kids don't look well. They are always asking for snacks but they do not seem to like the food she gives them. Angela always eats well.
- The nurse at the clinic (near Angela's mum's) who saw Michelle, thought she looked underweight and lethargic. She mentioned it to the health visitor, Bridget McCoy, at the end of the clinic when they were putting away the notes.
- Angela called in at the Michelsham Health Centre and asked to see Samina Khan. Samina was out. The receptionist asked her if she would like to see anyone else. She said no and went.
- Angela finds it hard to fill the mornings. Ricky is usually bursting with energy and disruptive in the flat. She never gets a chance to play with the baby. She has to give all her attention to Ricky. She took him to the library once when it was raining but he threw the books about.
- Bridget McCoy has twice called at Angela's mum's house and got no reply. She left a card for Angela each time.
- Michelle tumbled down a flight of concrete steps in the flats at 3.00 pm on Tuesday 28th. Angela had let her push the buggy up and down the landing and kept an eye on her through the open door. Michelle pushed the buggy to the top of the stairs and tumbled down, banging her head badly. It was a few moments before she screamed. Her arm was wrenched and she had banged her back.
- On Tuesday 28th no-one came to collect Ricky from the nursery at 3.30. Mrs Bessamy had no number for Des and at 4.20 pm, Mrs Bessamy knocked at Angela's door – no reply. At 4.40 pm the nursery phoned social services.
- Angela took Michelle to Casualty at the hospital after she fell on Tuesday 28th. She pushed a note under Janice's door asking her to collect Ricky and rushed to the hospital. The hospital examined her and took x-rays, asked how it had happened and how the old bruises had happened. They both had to stay in the play room for observation.
- At 5.00 pm last Tuesday, Angela phoned the nursery to ask if Daniel's mum, Janice, had collected Ricky. She had not. The nursery staff were very worried but understood now what had happened. They agreed to see if Janice would look after Ricky till Angela got back.

- The hospital let Angela take Michelle home at 6.30. They said she should be fine; that Angela had gone the right thing in bringing her in; to bring her back if any of the symptoms listed on a card happened; and that they would send a letter to Angela's GP and Health Visitor. Angela got home just before 7.00 pm. She collected Ricky from Janice who was really nice to her and understanding . . .

TASK 1:
REVIEW

Discuss the following:

1 In making your assessment, how confident are you that you have the full picture?

2 Which bits of information were most important to you in building up this picture?

3 How different would your view have been if this information had been missing?

4 How easy was it for you to make your assessment?

5 In this exercise, all the people with the information were in one room. In real life, who might have jumped to the wrong conclusions and why?

6 Can you think of any way to encourage information sharing and teamwork between people working with children and young families?

Part 2: Looking for support

What support and services can you suggest for Angela and her children? You will need to refer to the cards in these tasks.

TASK 2:
WHAT'S THE
PROBLEM?

Whatever you decided in Part 1, you will probably have concluded that Angela's problems have got worse. They need a lot of disentangling.

In pairs, look back at Activity 2 of the Case Study on page 40. Here you identified Angela's **problems, practical steps** to help her with them and **who** could offer this help. Assume that none of this happened and you now have the task of suggesting support and services for Angela.

(a) Take a whole sheet of paper. Write Angela's name in the middle and jot down the problems around the page as you spot them. You may find it helpful to group them.

(b) Pool your ideas as a whole group.

TASK 3:
A PLAN OF ACTION

As before, divide a sheet of paper into three columns headed 'Problems'; 'Practical steps', and 'Who?'

TASK 4:
PROBLEM SOLVING

In pairs, each take a major problem area and see what you can suggest to help Angela. Refer to the Service Checklist on p 34. Areas you might research include

- financial

- check her Income Support entitlement
- what can you suggest about her debts?
- can you make suggestions about budgeting?
- nursery/childcare provision
  - could she be offered more for Ricky?
  - what can you suggest for Michelle?
- social and family relationships
  - is there any scope for support or help here?
- using services
  - can you sort her out a regular health visitor? A GP she sees? How is this done? Should she see someone regularly? Who?
- local facilities
  - can you make realistic suggestions about things to do and places to go that she can afford?

Follow up work

This assignment could be an introduction to, or outcome of a topic in child protection and family support. Follow-up work could include:

(a) What procedures are followed at a day nursery to monitor a child at risk?

(b) What support is available to families under stress in your area?

(c) Under what circumstances are children taken into care? What are the procedures for this?

(d) What provision is there for children in care in your area? Foster care? Children's homes?

Assignment 14:
Danger at home

HOW DO deaths and injuries in the home compare with those on the roads at work?

DEATH AT HOME	5,700	INJURY AT HOME*	3,000,000
DEATH ON THE ROAD	5,500	INJURY ON THE ROAD*	320,000
DEATH AT WORK	600	INJURY AT WORK**	300,000

Figures represent yearly estimates
*Injuries requiring hospital or other medical treatment
**Report injuries

Some facts and figures

★ The biggest single cause of accidents is HUMAN ERROR.

★ Most accidents can be prevented with forethought.
★ More people are injured in their homes than anywhere else.
★ Home accidents account for 40% of all fatal accidents and one-third of all

non-fatal accidents requiring hospital treatment.

⋆ The kitchen, living or dining area, garden, stairs and bedrooms are potentially very dangerous places.

⋆ FALLS, of one kind or another, account for 40% of all home accidents.

⋆ FIRE is one of the most serious hazards in any home.

'IMPACT' Accidents

These account for an incredible 65% of home accident cases. Mainly falls, but they also include cuts, being hurt by falling objects and general 'bumping into' type accidents. The elderly are particularly at risk from falls.

'HEAT' Accidents

Not occurring as frequently as accidents in the above category, but accidents of this type can be particularly nasty with very serious consequences. Injuries include scalds and burns. Burns are usually the result of contact from a 'controlled' heat source such as a kettle. Firemen also attend 60,000 home fires each year where the main sources of ignition are from cooking fat, misused and/or faulty electrical appliances and wiring and smoker's materials.

'THROUGH MOUTH' Accidents

This category includes accidental poisonings, suffocation and choking. Children are especially vulnerable here as they are likely to put all manner of objects into their mouths.

Children (0–15 years)

The 'human' factor in accidents to children may include one or, more likely, several of the following:-

poor parental/adult supervision, small physical stature, stress or upset (possibly brought about by family argument, illness, trouble at school, etc), curiosity, showing off and taking risks, spirit of adventure, ignorance of the world and its dangers, lack of knowledge and training.

Children, until the age of at least 12 years, have not sufficiently developed their powers of logical reasoning to be able to know and understand what danger is

and how to deal with it when it arises. They need, therefore, very careful adult supervision, particularly when very young.

Adults

The 'human' factor in accidents to adults may be due to any combination of the following:-

impatience, carelessness, stress, fatigue, absentmindedness (possibly linked to stress and tiredness), negligence, irresponsible behaviour, taking risks, spirit of adventure, inadequate knowledge and training, sudden illness, the ageing factor, alcohol, drugs and medicines, a general disregard for personal health and safety.

The non-human face of accidents

Other contributory factors may include:

Mechanical defects: faulty appliances, poorly designed products, poor house wiring, gas leaks, etc. Poor lighting in the home could contribute to people having falls.

(Extracts taken from the RoSPA *Guide to projects in home safety.* Reproduced by kind permission of the Royal Society for the Prevention of Accidents)

TASK 1: FACTS AND FIGURES

Study the above extract from *The RoSPA Guide to Home Safety* and answer the following questions:

(*a*) What percentage of all fatal accidents occurs at home? How many fatalities is this?

(*b*) How many injuries requiring medical treatment happen at home each year? What percentage of non-fatal accidents needing hospital treatment happens at home?

(*c*) Which areas of the home are the most dangerous?

(*d*) What is an 'impact accident'?

(*e*) Who is particularly at risk from falls? Why do you think this is?

(*f*) How do accidents from heat usually occur?

(*g*) Who is most vulnerable to 'through mouth' accidents? Why do you think this is?

(*h*) Many causes for accidents involving adults are suggested. Which three do you think are the most relevant to your age group?

(*i*) Which two causes of accidents involving children do you think are the most important?

(*j*) How do the figures for accidents at home compare with those on the road or at work?

TASK 2: PERSONAL EXPERIENCE

(*a*) Find out what accidents the members of your group have experienced, either themselves, or to someone close to them.

(*b*) Divide these into the RoSPA groupings:

- At home
- On the road
- At work

Draw a bar chart to show the distribution of these accidents. Compare your results with RoSPA's figures.

(*c*) Divide the 'accidents at home' category into type of accident, again using RoSPA's groupings

- Impact
- Heat
- Through mouth

Draw a pie chart to show the proportions of accidents in each category.

TASK 3: THINKING SAFETY

Each picture opposite shows a danger in the home. Taking each picture in turn, state:

(*a*) What accident might happen;

(*b*) What action to take that instant to prevent the accident;

(*c*) Precautions to take to prevent this incident happening again; and

(*d*) What to do if the accident happens.

TASK 4: DO YOU KNOW WHAT TO DO?

Answer these multiple choice questions to test yourself

1 An elderly woman you are visiting splashes her hand and scalds herself as she makes you a cup of tea. What do you do immediately:

(*a*) Apply cream.

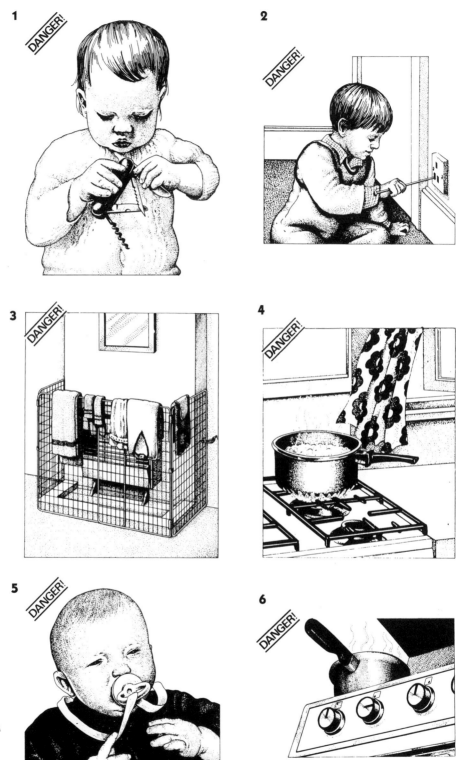

(Taken from *Play it Safe! A guide to preventing children's accidents*, published by the Health Education Authority)

(*b*) Call the doctor.

(*c*) Immerse in cold water.

(*d*) Wrap the scald in a bandage.

2 A four-year-old tipped up off a trolley at your nursery and banged his head on the concrete. It was a few moments before he started to cry and a nasty bruise is already appearing. How do you react?

(*a*) Rush him to hospital.

(*b*) Watch him, and if he appears drowsy or sick seek medical aid.

(*c*) Keep him awake for the next eight hours.

(*d*) Apply a cold compress to the bruise.

(*e*) Let him go to sleep and see how he is when he wakes up.

3 A woman working in the kitchen with you cuts herself badly on the arm with a knife. It is bleeding freely. What do you do?

(*a*) Apply direct pressure to the wound.

(*b*) Apply a tourniquet to stop the bleeding.

(*c*) Wash the cut.

(*d*) Apply a loose bandage.

4 A colleague at work has a bad nose bleed. What would be the best course of action?

(*a*) Plug the nose with cotton wool.

(*b*) Blow the nose to clear the bleeding.

(*c*) Lay the person flat on the floor.

(*d*) Apply pressure to the nose and hold the head forward.

5 You find your client you are visiting unconscious and in contact with a cable from an electric fan heater. What do you do immediately?

(*a*) Pull the client away.

(*b*) Switch off the electricity supply.

(*c*) Check that the client still has a pulse.

(*d*) Move the fire away.

6 What immediate action would you take if someone in your care had an epileptic fit?

(*a*) Slap them on the face.

(*b*) Place them on their back with their head turned to one side.

(*c*) Put smelling salts under their nose.

(*d*) Sit them in a straight backed chair.

7 An elderly person in your care trips over a mat and falls down badly banging his hip. What do you do?

(*a*) Move him so that he is comfortable.

(*b*) Give him a drink.

(*c*) Call an ambulance.

(*d*) Cover him with a blanket to keep warm.

8 A toddler is found with an empty bottle of asprins. You cannot see them on the floor and assume the child has swallowed them. What do you do immediately?

(*a*) Make the child sick.

(*b*) Give the child a glass of milk to dilute the tablets.

(*c*) Seek medical aid.

(*d*) Check the child's pulse and temperature and seek medical aid if abnormal.

9 A client in your care trips and falls on her arm. You suspect that it is broken. What do you do?

(*a*) Help the client to stand up.

(*b*) Call an ambulance.

(*c*) Put the arm gently across the chest and support with a sling.

(*d*) Feel the arm to see whether it is definitely broken.

10 A baby has pulled a button off her coat and put it in her mouth. She is choking. What do you do immediately?

(*a*) Hold her by the ankles and shake her vigorously.

(*b*) Lay her on her stomach and apply pressure to her back.

(*c*) Insert two fingers in her mouth to make her sick.

(*d*) Supporting her, head down, slap her briskly between the shoulder blades.

Check your answers on page 286.

TASK 5:
SAFETY FOR CLIENTS

1 (*a*) What accidents are most likely to happen in the households of
- Angela Williams (CS1)
- Gladys Miller (CS4)
- Rose MacDonald (CS5)
- Nellie Taylor (CS6)

(*b*) What precautions should be taken routinely to prevent them.

Present your discussion in two columns headed 'Hazards' and 'Precautions'.

2 Fire would be a certain hazard for the residents of Firbank Road. Most smoke, all have learning difficulties, are new to catering for themselves in the kitchen, and none have had a private room before.

(*a*) Discuss the hazards from fire that you can identify in this situation.

(*b*) Design a poster to alert the residents of Firbank Road to the danger you consider to be most serious. It must convey a simple and eye-catching message.

Assignment 15:
Health and safety for care workers

Health care premises are dangerous places, unless everyone who works there helps to keep them safe. The legal responsibility for an employee's health and safety at work is shared between the employer and employee; you are required to know what you have to do. The most important pieces of legislation setting out these responsiblities are

- The Health and Safety at Work Act 1974
- The Control of Substances Hazardous to Health regulations 1989 (COSHH)

In the first tasks of this assignment you are asked to understand what is contained in the Acts, and find out how they apply to your workplace. Other tasks look at practical aspects of your health and safety at work.

Health and Safety Law

What you should know

Your health, safety and welfare at work are protected by law. Your employer has a duty to protect you and to keep you informed about health and safety. You have a responsibility to look after yourself and others. If there is a problem, discuss it with your employer or your safety representative, if there is one.

Your employer has a duty under the law, to ensure so far as is reasonably practicable, your health, safety and welfare at work.

In general, your employer's duties include:

- making your workplace safe and without risks to health;
- keeping dust, fume and noise under control;
- ensuring plant and machinery are safe and that safe systems of work are set and followed;
- ensuring articles and substances are moved, stored and used safely;
- providing adequate welfare facilities;
- giving you the information, instruction, training and supervision necessary for your health and safety.

Your employer must also:

- draw up a health and safety policy statement if there are 5 or more employees, including the health and safety organisation and arrangements in force, and bring it to your attention;
- provide free, any protective clothing or equipment specifically required by health and safety law;
- report certain injuries, diseases and dangerous occurrences to the enforcing authority;
- provide adequate first-aid facilities;
- consult a safety representative, if one is appointed by a recognised trade union, about matters affecting your health and safety;
- set up a safety committee if asked in writing by 2 or more safety representatives.

Employers also have duties to take precautions against fire, provide adequate means of escape and means for fighting fire.

As an employee, you have legal duties too. They include:

- taking reasonable care for your own health and safety and that of others who may be affected by what you do or do not do;
- cooperating with your employer on health and safety;
- not interfering with or misusing anything provided for your health, safety or welfare.

If you think there is a health and safety problem in your workplace you should first discuss it with your employer, supervisor or manager. You may also wish to discuss it with your safety representative, if there is one.

TASK 1:
AT WORK
WITH HEALTH
AND SAFETY

With a partner read the guide to the Health and Safety at Work Act 1974, and answer the following questions.

(a) How are dust, fumes and noise kept under control at your work place? Find out in detail how **one** of these is controlled. You may find it helpful to find out the cleaning routine of a clinical area.

(b) Find out one 'safe system' of work for a procedure you might be involved in.

(c) Identify one 'article' and one 'substance' that is regularly moved, stored and used in your workplace. What safety procedures are followed?

(d) What do you think is meant by 'adequate welfare facilities'? What welfare facilities are there at your workplace? Do you think these are 'adequate'?

(e) Have you had any health and safety training? If so, explain what this was. If not, explain why you think none has been offered.

(f) Collect a copy of the health and safety policy from your work place.

(g) Do you wear any protective clothing? What purpose does it serve?

(h) What 'injuries, diseases and dangerous occurrences' have been reported to the 'enforcing authorities'? Who are these 'enforcing authorities'?

(i) What are your first aid facilities?

(j) Do you have a safety representative? Who is this and how were they appointed?

(k) What precautions have been taken against fire at your work place?

(l) What are **your** legal duties to contribute towards your own health and safety?

HAVE YOU BEEN COSHHED?

The Control of Substances Hazardous to Health regulations came into force on 1st October 1989.

They are designed to protect YOU but can only work with YOUR INVOLVEMENT.

YOUR EMPLOYERS

- Will assess the risks to health in your workplace
- If possible, prevent anyone being exposed to dangerous substances, or . . .
- Control exposure to reduce any risk
- Train and inform YOU

YOUR RESPONSIBILITIES

- Know the risks involved
- Know all instructions given
- Use all necessary safety equipment
- Report any faults or potential hazards

REMEMBER! YOUR SAFETY IS YOUR RESPONSIBILITY

**TASK 2:
HAVE YOU
BEEN COSHHED?**

Study the COSHH regulations above and answer the following questions.

(a) What **are** the risks to health in your workplace? Care workers can be at risk from back strain, violence, skin conditions (e.g. dermatitis), fatigue, hepatitis, coughs and colds – but hopefully not all at once!

Find out what the people you work with consider to be the greatest health hazards in your workplace. You could do this by carrying out a formal or informal survey.

(b) Write down a clear set of instructions for using one potentially hazardous substance in use at your workplace.

(*c*) What safety equipment is in use for dealing with one hazardous substance at your workplace?

Draw a simple diagram of it and explain how it works. Show the stages of its working by numbers linking your diagram with your text.

TASK 3:
SAFETY AUDIT

Many trade union safety representatives now use a safety audit checklist, such as the one shown below, as a basis for checking that workplaces are safe. A checklist for particular health care settings may include more specific points to check.

Example of a safety audit checklist

	YES	NO
A Entrance halls, staircases and passages		
Is lighting adequate?		
Are all lights working?		
Are escape routes identified?		
Are they free from obstruction?		
Is there fire fighting equipment?		
Is it adequate and in working order?		
Are floors clean and dry?		
Are electric sockets, plugs and leads undamaged and in working order?		
Are lifts or stairs and/or lifts free from obstruction?		
Are they undamaged?		
B Rooms for clients/patients		
Are they free from rubbish?		
Are exits clear from obstruction?		
Are escape doors easily identified?		
Are lights adequate?		
Are they in working order?		
Are floors clean and dry?		
Are materials stored safely and tidily?		
Are electric sockets, plugs and leads undamaged and in working order?		
Are fires adequately protected and in working order?		
Are pipes and cables protected and undamaged?		
Is there enough space for people and equipment to move around safely and easily?		
C Toilets		
Are all appliances kept clean and undamaged?		
Are all doors, locks and catches in working order?		
Is there a supply of soap, towels and toilet rolls?		
Are all lights in working order?		
Are bins for used paper and soiled dressings emptied regularly?		
D Kitchens		
Is the lighting adequate?		
Is ventilation adequate?		
Is the water supply adequate?		

	YES	NO
Are the floors kept clean and dry?		
Is there any equipment not working properly?		
Are there guards on dangerous machines?		
Is rubbish stored in suitable bins and emptied regularly?		
Is fire fighting equipment in working order?		
Are notices displayed? e.g. no smoking, fire drill.		
Are knives stored correctly?		
Do the staff wear suitable protective clothing?		
Is food stored correctly?		
Is any food exposed or left standing?		
Are soap, nail brush and clean towels available at each wash hand basin?		
Are all surfaces undamaged, clean and free from grease?		
Is there any grease build-up on cooking equipment?		
Is there any evidence of vermin or insects?		
Are chemical cleaning agents stored properly in a lockable cupboard?		
Is the temperature reasonable?		

(a) Draw up your own list and, with a partner, complete a safety audit of your workplace or college.

(b) Report on health and safety in your college or work place. Agree with your tutor and partner what form this should take; whether verbal, written, in note form or in full.

In your report identify the areas where you can see that health and safety issues have been thought about and where there is room for improvement.

Conclude your report with recommendations for changes you would like to see to improve health and safety in the building.

Note:
Before attempting this section, you must have received some practical training in lifting from someone *qualified* to instruct you. This is an instruction that you must not ignore in the interests of your own health and safety!

TASK 4:
MIND YOUR BACK!

Under the Health and Safety Act you have to take 'reasonable care of your own health and safety and that of others who might be affected by what you do.' This includes looking after your back to minimise the risk of back injuries. This means using the correct lifting techniques.

1 Read the advice for lifting and moving patients 'Moving the patient' on pp 159–161, and the instructions for
   ● Sitting the patient up
   ● Lifting the patient from bed to chair
   ● Helping the patient up from a chair.
   and answer the following questions.
   (a) Why should you make sure that the floor is clear?

MOVING THE PATIENT

PROTECTING YOURSELF FROM INJURY

Moving a patient can cause you serious back injury if he is too heavy. Try to have a helper or mechanical aid available, and always follow these guidelines:
- clear the floor space
- keep your back straight: avoid arching it backwards or forwards
- bend your knees, not your back

- make your thigh muscles do the work
- wear supporting shoes with low heels
- always lift towards you, never away from you: this gives you better control.

Encourage the patient to cooperate. Always *lift* him up the bed: never drag him. The following lifts are designed to protect you from injury.

SITTING UP THE PATIENT

You will want to sit the patient up for meals and as a change of position, but this is also the first step in lifting her or moving her from the bed to a chair.

1 Fold the patient's arms across her waist. Place your inside knee on the bed level with her hip, and your outside foot on the floor in line with her waist. With your knee bent, put both hands well under her shoulder blades.

2 Keeping your arms straight sit back on your heels, letting your body weight lift the patient to the sitting position. If the patient is now going to get up or into a chair, with one hand supporting her back help her to swing her legs over the side of the bed.

(Taken from *Caring for the Sick* published for St John Ambulance by Dorling Kindersley)

LIFTING THE PATIENT FROM A BED TO A CHAIR WITH A HELPER

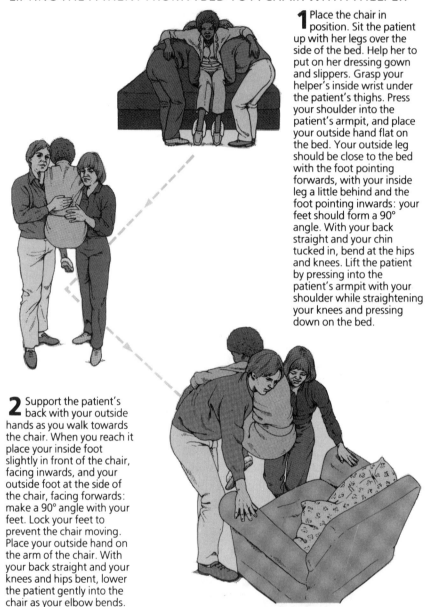

1 Place the chair in position. Sit the patient up with her legs over the side of the bed. Help her to put on her dressing gown and slippers. Grasp your helper's inside wrist under the patient's thighs. Press your shoulder into the patient's armpit, and place your outside hand flat on the bed. Your outside leg should be close to the bed with the foot pointing forwards, with your inside leg a little behind and the foot pointing inwards: your feet should form a 90° angle. With your back straight and your chin tucked in, bend at the hips and knees. Lift the patient by pressing into the patient's armpit with your shoulder while straightening your knees and pressing down on the bed.

2 Support the patient's back with your outside hands as you walk towards the chair. When you reach it place your inside foot slightly in front of the chair, facing inwards, and your outside foot at the side of the chair, facing forwards: make a 90° angle with your feet. Lock your feet to prevent the chair moving. Place your outside hand on the arm of the chair. With your back straight and your knees and hips bent, lower the patient gently into the chair as your elbow bends.

(b) How can you protect your back from strain?

(c) What are 'supporting shoes with low heels'? Why are these recommended?

(d) Why should you tell the patient what you are doing?

(e) Why should you always turn the patient towards you?

(f) How do you hold your arms to help a patient sit up?

(g) How should your feet be positioned when two people lift a patient (i) from the bed; and (ii) into a chair? Why is this?

(h) When you help a patient up from a chair, what can you do to stop them sliding forward?

HELPING THE PATIENT UP FROM A CHAIR

1 Stand slightly to one side of the patient and put one foot in front of hers to stop her sliding forwards. Make sure the chair cannot move. Bend your legs at the knee and place your hands under her armpits.

2 Keeping your back straight, straighten your legs and bring the patient into the standing position. Make sure she is steady before you move your feet and allow her to walk.

(Taken from *Caring for the Sick* published for St John Ambulance by Dorling Kindersley)

2 Try these lifting techniques in groups of four. Take it in turns to be
- the instructor
- the observer
- the care worker
- the patient

The instructor: Give the instructions slowly and accurately. The care worker can ask you questions when they are unsure.

The observer: You should say nothing but watch what happens. Note the comfort of the patient; how instructions are given and followed; things you think were particularly well done and where there is room for improvement. Feed back your observations to your group.

The patient: Imagine that you want to move but cannot. Do not help the care worker too much, but do not be obstructive!

The care worker: Follow the instructions you are given. Ask questions if you are unsure. Pay special attention to the comfort of the patient.

    (*a*) Did you feel strain in any part of your body?

    (*b*) Did your clothes make any movement awkward?

    (*c*) Did you find it easy to say the right sorts of things to the patient?

    (*d*) What was the hardest part of the activity?

**TASK 5:
THE POCKET GUIDE**

Draw up a list of 'DOs' and 'DON'Ts' for preventing back injuries. Present it as a post card-sized pocket guide for people new to lifting.

Your information must be clear and concise and presented so it will not be forgotten.

TASK 6:
THE FIRST AID BOX

Employers have a duty to provide 'adequate first aid facilities'. In many workplaces this includes a first aid box.

1 The British Red Cross suggests that a first aid box should contain the items shown in the table below. Does the first aid box at your work place or college contain them? Check the contents of your workplace first aid box against the Red Cross list, copy out the table below and tick off each item in column 2.

Column 1 **Red Cross suggested contents**	Column 2 **Your box**	Column 3 **Cost**

Different sized
   sterile dressings
Assortment of
   adhesive dressings
A few 25g rolls
   of cotton wool
Packet of antiseptic
   wipes
2 crepe or conforming
   bandages
Selection of safety
   pins
Tweezers
Pair of blunt-
   ended scissors		

Total		£ _____

2 Go to a chemist and price the items in the Red Cross list. How much would it cost to make up a first aid box for your home?

Assignment 16:
Fire!

Note to tutor: You might like to link this assignment with a routine fire drill in your premises.

TASK 1:
THE FIRE
SAFETY PLAN

Your group has the responsibility to evacuate the building you are in now in the event of a fire.

1 (a) Identify the tasks that would have to be done.

(b) Allocate specific duties to each member of your group.

(c) When you have a provisional plan, allocate about 15 minutes for the group to go and check their duties to see if you have overlooked any difficulty.

(d) Finalise your fire safety plan.

2 There should be a fire safety plan at your workplace. Each member of staff should have specific duties. What are they? What are yours?

TASK 2:
SAFETY SIGNS

Study 'the great escape' safety signs on p 165.

(a) What do 'prohibition' and 'mandatory' mean?

(b) What is the significance of the colour and shape of safety signs?

(c) Go round your building and see how many of the different colours of fire extinguisher you see.

(d) Go round the building and see how many safety signs in each of the five categories you see. Which are they? Make sketches of them.

TASK 3:
EMERGENCY
ESCAPE ROUTES

If there was a fire in your building, how would you get out? At your workplace, how would you evacuate the vulnerable people in your charge?

Your task is to draw a plan of the floor of the building you work in, or the building you are in at present, showing the emergency escape routes. Copy out the signs and symbols and use these on your plan to show the key points these signs show.

You will need a large sheet of paper for a scale drawing. Work in pairs.

What CAUSES fires in health care premises?

There are 4 BASIC CAUSES OF FIRES:

CARELESS SMOKING

Most fires are caused by careless handling of smoking materials by staff, patients or visitors.

TO REDUCE THE DANGER:

- Enforce all smoking rules.
- Provide proper ashtrays.
- Empty ashtrays frequently, checking for live ashes.
- Smoke only in recognised areas.

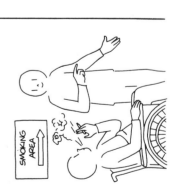

PRESSURISED OXYGEN

Used improperly, oxygen can cause an explosion or can intensify an already burning fire.

TO REDUCE THE DANGER:

- Store oxygen cylinders in designated storage areas, with valve caps in place.
- Never smoke around oxygen.
- If authorised, periodically test valves, hose connections and regulators for leaks.
- Use only special electrically-safe equipment in areas where oxygen is in use.

FLAMMABLE LIQUIDS and GASES

Many materials used in routine cleaning and maintenance can ignite or explode if used carelessly.

TO REDUCE THE DANGER:

- Store flammables in approved safety containers that are clearly labelled. Place containers in designated metal cabinets, away from heat.
- Never smoke around flammables.
- Store compressed gas cylinders separately, away from heat, with protective caps in place.

ELECTRICAL EQUIPMENT

Electrical equipment like hair-dryers, razors (if allowed) can be a fire hazard if in bad condition or if used improperly.

TO REDUCE THE DANGER:

- Check wires for broken, crushed, cracked, brittle or frayed insulation and other defects.
- Don't overload outlets.
- Don't run leads under rugs.

If in any doubt, have a qualified electrician check to ensure that patients' and staff's personal appliances are in safe condition and properly earthed.

(Taken from *Fire Safety in Health Care Premises,* published by the Wandsworth Health Authority)

the great escape

WATER CO₂ SODA ACID	DRY POWDER	FOAM	CO₂ CARBON DIOXIDE	VAPOURISING LIQUIDS
RED	**BLUE**	**CREAM**	**BLACK**	**GREEN**
WOOD, PAPER TEXTILES etc.	FLAMMABLE LIQUIDS	FLAMMABLE LIQUIDS	FLAMMABLE LIQUIDS	FLAMMABLE LIQUIDS
UNSAFE ALL VOLTAGES	**SAFE ALL VOLTAGES**	**UNSAFE ALL VOLTAGES**	**SAFE ALL VOLTAGES**	**SAFE ALL VOLTAGES**

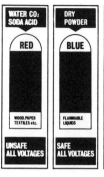

TYPE ▸	PROHIBITION	MANDATORY	WARNING	SAFE CONDITION	FIRE EQUIPMENT
MEANING ▸	You must not. Do not do. Stop.	You must do. Carry out the action given by the sign.	Caution. Risk of danger. Hazard ahead.	The safe way. Where to go in an emergency.	To indicate fire equipment.
SHAPE & COLOUR ▸	OUTLINE CIRCLE WITH CROSS BAR — RED means STOP	SOLID CIRCLE — BLUE means OBEY	OUTLINE TRIANGLE — YELLOW means risk of DANGER	RECTANGLE — GREEN means GO	RECTANGLE — RED means Fire Equipment
EXAMPLE ▸					

Safety signs (as specified by
the Safety Signs Regulations 1980)

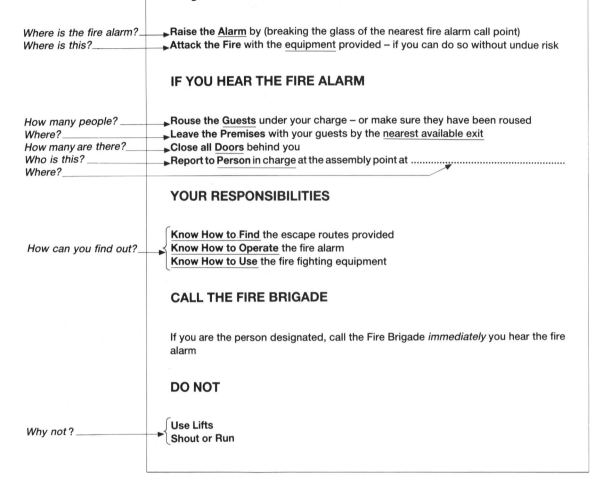

A SPECIMEN NOTICE TO STAFF

FIRE RULES
If you discover a fire

Where is the fire alarm? → **Raise the Alarm** by (breaking the glass of the nearest fire alarm call point)
Where is this? → **Attack the Fire** with the equipment provided – if you can do so without undue risk

IF YOU HEAR THE FIRE ALARM

How many people? → **Rouse the Guests** under your charge – or make sure they have been roused
Where? → **Leave the Premises** with your guests by the nearest available exit
How many are there? → **Close all Doors** behind you
Who is this? → **Report to Person** in charge at the assembly point at ....
Where?

YOUR RESPONSIBILITIES

How can you find out? → **Know How to Find** the escape routes provided
Know How to Operate the fire alarm
Know How to Use the fire fighting equipment

CALL THE FIRE BRIGADE

If you are the person designated, call the Fire Brigade *immediately* you hear the fire alarm

DO NOT

Why not? → **Use Lifts**
Shout or Run

TASK 4:
FIRE RULES

A notice such as the one shown above should be displayed in your college or workplace. Have you ever read it properly?

Make a copy of the fire rules in your establishment, and add in the answers to the questions highlighted above.

TASK 5:
EVACUATE!

1 Study the methods of carrying patients shown opposite.
2 Divide into four groups.
   • Group 1 can move and walk with difficulty but unaided

REMOVING PATIENTS

When fire threatens an incapacitated patient, he or she must be evacuated quickly and safely. Staff members should learn and practice these PATIENT CARRIES. (The one you choose will depend on patient's condition, your strength, time, etc.) These are just a few of those available.

ONE-PERSON CARRIES

HUMAN CRUTCH*

1. Stand at patient's injured side.

2. Place victim's arm around your neck. Hold patient's hand with your free hand.

3. Place your other arm around patient's waist. Hold onto patient's clothing at hip.

* Do not use this method if patient's upper limb(s) is injured.

BLANKET DRAG

1. Fold a blanket in half length-wise and place it on the floor beside the bed.

2. Slide one arm under the patient's neck and shoulders and the other under patient's knees.

3. Pull patient to the end of the bed, drop down to one knee and lower patient so that your knee supports patient's back.

4. Let patient slide gently to the blanket and pull from room head first on blanket.

TWO-PERSON CARRIES

2- or 4-HANDED CARRY

1. The first person raises the patient to a sitting position at the edge of the bed and places one arm behind patient's shoulder and the other arm under patient's knees.

2. The second person places one arm behind the patient and grasps the first person's shoulder, then places the other arm under the patient's knees and grasps the first person's wrist.

3. Patient sits on rescuers' clasped hands and wrists and leans back against their arms.

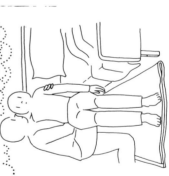

FORE AND AFT CARRY

1. The first person raises the patient to a sitting position, then, from behind, reaches under the patient's armpits and grasps his or her own wrists in front of patient's chest.

2. The second person moves between the patient's legs with his or her back to the patient and encircles the patient's legs at the knees with each arm.

3. The first person hugs and lifts, the second carries patient's legs, and patient is moved feet first.

(Taken from *Fire Safety in Health Care Premises*, published by the Wandsworth Health Authority)

- Group 2 can walk with help
- Group 3 cannot walk at all
- Group 4 are the staff who have to get Groups 1, 2 and 3 out of the building to the assembly point.

At an agreed moment evacuate your classroom.

3 **Review:** How long did it take? What problems were there?

Assignment 17: Practical hygiene

As a care worker you have a double responsibility for hygiene and cleanliness – your own and that of your clients and their surroundings.

TASK 1:
BEING CLEAN

1   Discussion point: What aspects of personal hygiene do you think are important? List them all on a board or flipchart and then in pairs number them in order of importance, starting with the most important.

2   (a) Copy out the table shown below and tick the column to show which aspects of personal hygiene you consider to be of little or no concern to others and which ones you decide a person should try and change.

	No concern to others	Should try to change
Uncleaned teeth		
Smelly feet		
Bad breath		
Dirty nails		
Unwashed face		
Long toe nails		
Bitten finger nails		
Dirty clothes		
Body odour		
Underarm hair		
Untidy hair		
Decaying teeth		
Runny nose		
Dirty hair		
Yesterday's make up		

(b) In small groups discuss the ways in which you could suggest that someone makes changes in the areas you have identified. This is a difficult thing to do, so think carefully. Make a note of strategies you agree could be used and then report back to the rest of the class.

TASK 2:
KEEPING CLEAN

Both at home and at work you will be aware of the time you spend on keeping yourself and your surroundings clean.

(a) Copy out the table below listing cleaning tasks and put a tick in the column to show how frequently you do each one. You will not be asked to show your list to anyone unless you choose to.

	Daily	Weekly	Infrequently
Clean teeth			
Have a bath			
Have a shower			
Wash hair			
Clear waste paper bins			
Wash feet			
Hoover			
Clean toilet			
Brush hair			
Wash sheets			
Clean windows			
Remove dust			
Remove grease and dirt from kitchen surfaces			
Clean fridge			
Clean nails			
Wash hands			
Clean ashtrays			
Wash armpits			

(b) Do you think that there should be 'hygiene rules' for these cleaning tasks, or is it purely a matter of personal taste? Does it make any difference if you are a care or healthcare worker?

TASK 3:
LEARNING
BY DOING

Most practical skills in caring are learnt through doing; demonstration by a skilled and experienced person; and practice by the learner. Many routines and procedures may seem rigid to a newcomer and the learner needs to know *why* something is done in a particular way in order to learn the skill effectively.

There are many of these practical skills; one is bedmaking. Care has to be taken to avoid cross-infection and cause as little disturbance as possible to the patient.

Making an empty bed. The following sentences have been scrambled but all refer to the pictures opposite. Regroup the sentences and put the relevant text under each picture.

● Place the bottom sheet right side up with the crease centred down the middle of the bed.

● Loosen the bedclothes at the end of the bed to enable the patient to move his or her feet without restrictions.

● Place the top sheet in position wrong side up, with the crease down the middle.

- Work in pairs if you can.
- Pull the sheet taut before tucking in the sides.
- Put pillows on the bed.
- Repeat with each blanket.
- Tuck in the sheet at the foot of the bed. Make mitred corners and tuck in all along the sides.
- Turn the top sheet down over the blankets and counterpane.
- Fold the bedclothes neatly into three, following one of the two methods illustrated, and place them on two chairs at the end of the bed in the order you will need them.
- Allow a 45 cm turnover and half cover the pillow.
- N.B. If using a duvet, shake it so the filling is evenly spread and lay it on the bottom sheet with no top sheet and no counterpane.
- Tuck in along the head, then the foot of the bed, making mitred corners.
- Place the counterpane on the bed with the sides hanging loose.

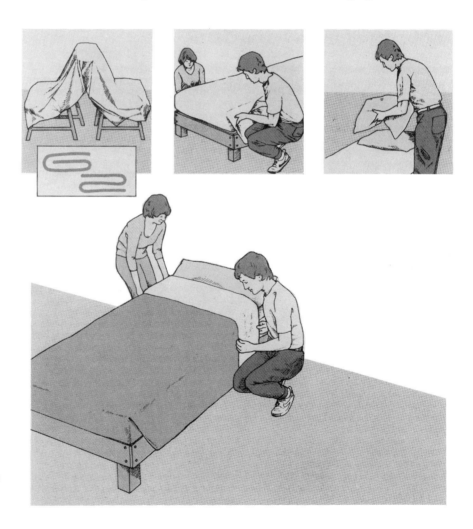

(Taken from *Caring for the Sick* published for St John Ambulance by Dorling Kindersley)

2   Bedmaking when the patient cannot get up.

(*a*) In pairs, match the pictures opposite to the instuctions showing the different stages in making a bed when a patient is still lying flat in the bed.

(*b*) Make brief notes of your own on how to make a bed. Instruct another pair on how to make a bed in hospital, explaining the reasons for what you do.

3   Teaching a skill

(*a*) Write down the sequence of something you know how to do which others in your group may not know. Bring in to the classroom the essential equipment to carry out this task. Some ideas; a way of doing hair/make up; laying a table; wiring a plug; setting a video; staring up a computer; organising a file; covering a book.

(*b*) Teach your partner your skill.

(*c*) When you are satisfied that your partner is competent, it is their turn to teach someone else. Your task is to observe them to check that they are giving competent instruction.

(*d*) *Review:* share your experience of learning and teaching a practical skill with the group. What did you find most helpful?

- How do *you* learn?
- How do *you* teach?

(*e*) Discuss how important each of the following is in learning a practical skill;

- Memory
- Understanding
- Doing.

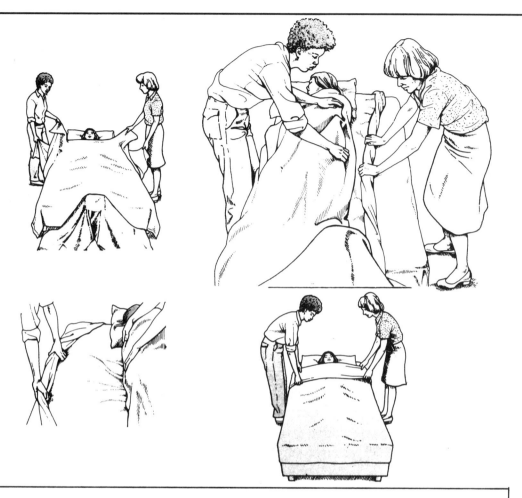

● Roll the patient to one side of the bed. Support her while your helper brushes out any crumbs, untucks the bottom layers of bedding and rolls them up to the patient's back. Your helper then straightens each layer in turn, pulling the underblanket and bottom sheet taut and tucking them in again.

● Sit the patient forward and replace the pillows. Unfold the top sheet over the blanket, then slide the blanket out from underneath, fold it and place on the chairs. Tuck in the sheet allowing 45cm turnover at the top. Replace the blankets one by one, tucking them in along the sides and more loosely at the foot of the bed. Replace the counterpane and turn down the sheet.

● Loosen the bedclothes all around the mattress. Remove the counterpane by folding it in three and place it on the chairs. Remove all except one blanket in the same way. Slide out the top sheet, leaving the patient covered with the blanket, fold it into three and put it on the chairs. Remove all but one pillow, and place on the chairs.

● Roll the patient gently to the other side of the bed. Your helper now supports her while you repeat the process.

Assignment 18:
Food hygiene

Food is headline news. At every stage from farming to consumption the headlines have highlighted what can – and does – go wrong. People who work with food **must** take these dangers seriously.

Once food has been harvested or slaughtered it begins to deteriorate so it is usually preserved for mass distribution. The effectiveness of this preservation depends upon correct storage and preparation. Even food that looks, smells and tastes quite normal can contain bacteria or viruses which can cause illness.

TASK 1:
SICKENING
STATISTICS

Look at these statistics published by *Which?* magazine, and answer the following questions.

(*a*) When were these figures published? Which year do they refer to?

(*b*) Roughly how many food poisoning cases were there in 1988, including unrecorded cases?

(*c*) What food items were contaminated?

(*d*) What different kinds of food poisoning are mentioned?

(*e*) How does 'large scale food production' contribute to increased levels of food poisoning?

Sickening statistics

● In 1988 there were 41,000 cases of food poisoning reported in the UK, compared with 30,000 in 1987. The full figures (including unrecorded cases) could be anything from five to 100 times as many.

● Large-scale food production can mean that a single contaminated source may affect many people. These are 1988 cases.

January More than 130 people had paratyphoid food poisoning caused by a contaminated lamb curry served at a celebration in Birmingham.

March Peperami salami sticks were linked to an outbreak of salmonella food poisoning; 74 people were affected.

May The House of Lords was hit: 85 people were affected, including 28 peers and 36 catering staff. The foods involved were egg-based, and were contaminated with *Salmonella typhimurium*.

July 38 people were ill with salmonella food poisoning at three Birmingham hospitals.

September 97 British tourists were taken ill with food poisoning while travelling home from the Costa Brava to Liverpool.

How the bugs can get into your food

Most of the food we eat has been through a number of hands (figuratively if not literally) on its way to your plate. Hygiene is important at all stages of the chain, including your kitchen. On this page, we take you through the farm-to-shop stages of the food chain, using chilled, ready-cooked chicken as an example, to show how bacteria can get into your food, and some steps producers can take to keep them out.

Cook-chill chicken chain

On the farm

It may never be possible to produce birds or other animals that do not harbour food poisoning bacteria, but good animal health is an important first step. The farmer needs good quality, uncontaminated animal feed from suppliers. The chickens need to be kept in hygienic conditions, and to be given clean water and feed if they are to stay healthy and uninfected.

At the slaughterhouse

Some chickens can carry harmful bacteria like salmonella yet look quite healthy. So, although sick birds are not sent for slaughter, some of these 'symptomless carriers' might be. If an infected bird leaves the farm for slaughtering, there is a risk that other chickens will be contaminated during the slaughter process.

Unless farm and slaughterhouse practices are improved, poultry will continue to be commonly infected with salmonella, campylobacter and/or listeria when it leaves the slaughterhouse. Some parts of chickens are more likely to be contaminated than others – the giblets, for example. If giblets are not handled carefully, they can contaminate the rest of the chicken.

In the factory

The chickens are then passed on to a factory for further processing. Storage, preparation and packaging in the factory can all present opportunities for bacteria to get into the product.

In a product that is cooked, chilled and then sold ready-to-eat, the most critical stage is after cooking in the factory. A physical barrier between the 'cooked' or 'high risk' area and the 'raw' area is advisable in factories for this type of product. The barrier is meant to stop staff, equipment or clothing from passing from the raw to the cooked area without being disinfected first.

Once the product has been cooked, it must be hygienically packaged, and cooled rapidly to stop bacteria growing. It is then kept chilled, ready for distribution.

On the lorries

Refrigerated lorries take the product from factory to shop. Many things can go wrong on the way, so the process needs to be carefully controlled. If the lorry or its refrigeration unit breaks down, temperatures can soon rise.

Unloading the products into a sunny loading bay can heat them up, and bacteria may grow before re-chilling slows them down again.

(Reproduced by kind
permission of *Which?*
magazine)

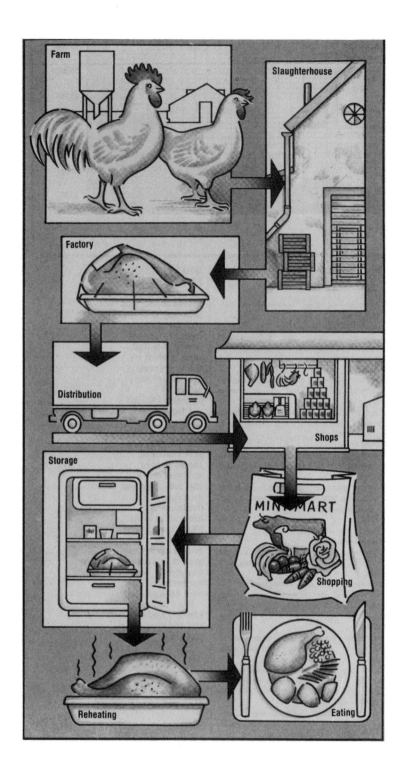

In the shops

When the product reaches the shop, quick transfer to a chill cabinet is vital to keep the product cool. If temperatures start to creep up, any bacteria that are present may grow. Regulations are in the pipeline to control the temperatures of chill cabinets in shops.

Retailers should also rotate stocks properly so that the oldest are sold first, and so that products are kept for as short a time as possible.

(Taken from *Which?* magazine April 1990)

**TASK 2:
HOW DOES FOOD
POISONING
HAPPEN?**

(*a*) Examine the notes on p 175 and the diagram opposite.
(*b*) Divide into five groups, one to consider each of the five farm-to-shop stages of the food chain. Your task is to produce a poster for each stage to highlight how bacteria can get into food and some steps to take to keep them out. You might like to add a sixth group to highlight hygiene in the kitchen.
(*c*) Present your finished poster to the whole group.

How to stop bacteria growth

Harmful bacteria come from
- infected animals – raw meat and poultry;
- the human body – our hands, noses, guts;
- insects and vermin
- dirt and waste.

To live and grow bacteria must have
- **Food**; especially the 'high risk' foods in the table on p 178.
- **Moisture**; dried foods and less vulnerable than fresh foods
- **Warmth**; they especially thrive at body temperature, 37°C, but the danger zone for growth is 10°C–63°C.
- **Time**; with warm, moist food, bacteria will reproduce every 10–20 minutes.

The bacteria that cause food poisoning are no exception. So to handle, store, prepare and serve food hygienically you have to
1   keep contamination out, through personal cleanliness, and cleanliness in the kitchen; and
2   prevent the growth of any bacteria that may be present by depriving them of the conditions they like.

**TASK 3:
HOW DO YOU
DO THIS?**

Fill in the table below to show how you would protect these 'high risk' foods from the conditions for bacteria growth if you were working in a large kitchen.

Food	Stop moisture	Stop warmth	Stop time
Meat & poultry			
Cooked meat			
Gravy stock, soup			
Milk & eggs			
Seafood			
Cooked rice			

TASK 4:
WHAT WOULD YOU
DO IF . . . ?

In pairs or small groups decide what you would do in each of the situations below.

(*a*) The hot dinners are served before some of the clients are ready. What do you do?

(*b*) You forget to bring your hat/hairnet to work while on kitchen duty? What do you do?

(*c*) The electricity goes off for the morning and you think about the fridge and freezer in the kitchen. What do you do?

(*d*) You cut your finger while making sandwiches. What do you do?

(*e*) A client tells you that her soup is cold. What do you do?

(*f*) Three biscuits fall from a plate you are carrying. What do you do?

(*g*) There is no room at the top of the fridge for your plate of cooked meat – the uncooked chicken is there. Where do you put your plate?

(*h*) You drop a knife on the floor as you are sorting cutlery. What do you do?

TASK 5:
WHAT TO DO
AND WHY

You may need to find out some of the information for these tasks, from a library, a textbook on food hygiene, or your tutor.

1 Below are a set of hygiene rules but no reasons for the rules are given. Your task is to add an explanation for each rule.

What should I do?

1 Wash your hands
- after using the lavatory
- between handling raw meat and cooked meat
- before and after touching food
- after coughing into your hands or using a handkerchief
- after touching your face or hair
- after carrying out any cleaning

2 Avoid touching your nose, coughing or sneezing over food.

3 Avoid touching food with your hands, whenever possible use tongs to handle food and plates or trays to carry it.

4 Keep hair covered with a net or disposable hat.

5 Keep fingernails short and clean.

6 Keep cuts, grazes and boils covered with a waterproof dressing that is brightly coloured – blue is a good colour.

7 Keep raw and cooked food separate, especially raw meat/poultry and cooked meat/poultry.

8 Clean kitchen utensils and equipment thoroughly, before and after use.

9 Keep food at the correct temperature – in storage and preparation
- Remember the 'high risk' foods
- Remember the temperature 'danger zone'.

10 Be sure that certain frozen food is thawed thoroughly before cooking – especially poultry and large joints of meat.

11 Keep food covered whenever possible.

12 Always ensure that the workplace is clean before preparing food.

(Taken from *Essential Food Hygiene* by Dr R J Donaldson and published by the Royal Society of Health)

2 **The hygiene quiz:** Below is a quiz based on one devised by *Which?* magazine inspectors. Complete it, working with a partner if you wish.

(*a*) Which two foods are the most common sources of food poisoning?
- (i)   Cheese and eggs
- (ii) Meat and poultry
- (iii) Fish and ham
- (iv) Fruit and vegetables

(*b*) What should you do after handling raw meat or poultry?
- (i)   Rinse your fingers under a tap
- (ii) Rinse the meat under a tap
- (iii) Wash your hands
- (iv) Wipe your hands

(*c*) How often should you change a used tea towel for a clean one?
- (i)   Daily
- (ii) Once a week
- (iii) Twice a day
- (iv) Once a month

(*d*) What temperature is the best for the growth of food poisoning bacteria?
- (i)   20°C
- (ii) 37°C
- (iii) 42°C
- (iv) 30°C

(*e*) At what temperature should a general purpose refrigerator operate?
- (i)   2°C–5°C
- (ii) 8°C–10°C
- (iii) 0°C–2°C
- (iv) 5°C–8°C

(*f*) For how long should you leave cooked meat to cool before putting it in the refrigerator?
- (i)   5 hours
- (ii) Half an hour
- (iii) 2 hours
- (iv) 1½ hours

(g) Which of the following foods should you never store together?
   (i)   Liver pâté and cheese
   (ii) Fried bacon and salami
   (iii) Ham and uncooked mince beef
   (iv) Raw chicken and uncooked sausages

Assignment 19: Good food

TASK 1:
WHY DO WE EAT
WHAT WE EAT?

Our eating habits are shaped by many influences such as:

- upbringing
- religion
- culture
- personal choice
- lifestyle
- budget
- time
- 'expert' advice
- commercial interests.

Which of these influences do you think are at work in the following comments?

- A proper meal is meat and two veg. It's got to be cooked.
- Fruit is too expensive. Salad too.
- I don't eat bread. It's fattening.
- I don't eat meat. I'm a Sikh.
- My children won't have anything to do with brown bread.
- I buy frozen veg. There's no waste.
- Spinach is good for you.
- A 'Mars' a day helps you work, rest and play.
- Butter, some say it's bad for you and others say it's OK.
- If I'm feeling down, I go and buy myself a cake.
- I fry in lard. You shouldn't, but it's cheap.
- I buy a stack of meals from Marks and Spencer. I don't know if it's expensive but we both work, and I don't have time to cook.
- Try our new fibre-enriched recipe.
- They made us eat cabbage at school. I haven't touched it since.
- I cut down on potatoes, but now they say they're good for you.
- It was always fish on Friday. Even now.
- My mum cooks Indian food at home, lots of dahl. But when I go out, we go to McDonalds.

- I haven't got time or money to cook fancy food.
- Eat 50 per cent less sugar.

(*a*) Do you recognise yourself in any of the comments above? Discuss.

(*b*) What are the influences that shape your own choice of food?

**TASK 2:
HEALTHY EATING**

(*a*) *'A guide to Healthy Eating'*, published by the Health Education Authority, will be very helpful to you in this assignment. Contact your local health education unit or write for a copy. If you write, do not forget to enclose a stamped addressed envelope.

(*b*) The booklet starts with the advice shown opposite.

The reasons for each of the five pieces of advice have been added. Read them carefully. Is there anything you did not know? Your task is to think of four tips on how to carry out this advice, and still eat tasty food. Copy out the table below and enter these tips in Column 2.

Column 1 **Aim**	Column 2 **4 tips on how to do it**	Column 3 **I could . . .**
Cut down on fat	1 2 3 4	
Cut down on sugar		
Cut down on salt		
Eat more fibre-rich foods		
Eat plenty of fresh fruit and vegetables		
Go easy on alcohol		
Get plenty of variety in what you eat.		

(*c*) Pool all the tips from members of the group. Choose one you think you could try for each 'healthy eating' aim and enter it in Column 3.

(*d*) Over the next week, try out each of the five tips you have chosen in your own choice of food or cooking. Report back to the group in a week's time to discuss the changes you made and what you thought of them. You may like to write up your experiences.

**TASK 3:
WHAT IS IN
YOUR FOOD?**

Most packaged foods show a list of **ingredients**, i.e. what has gone into your food listed in order of the amount used. Increasingly, food manufacturers are showing an analysis of the **nutritional value** of the food you buy.

1 Extract 1 on p 184 shows an analysis of the ingredients of Black Forest gateau.

(*a*) What is the largest ingredient?

(*b*) How many preservatives are there in glacé cherries?

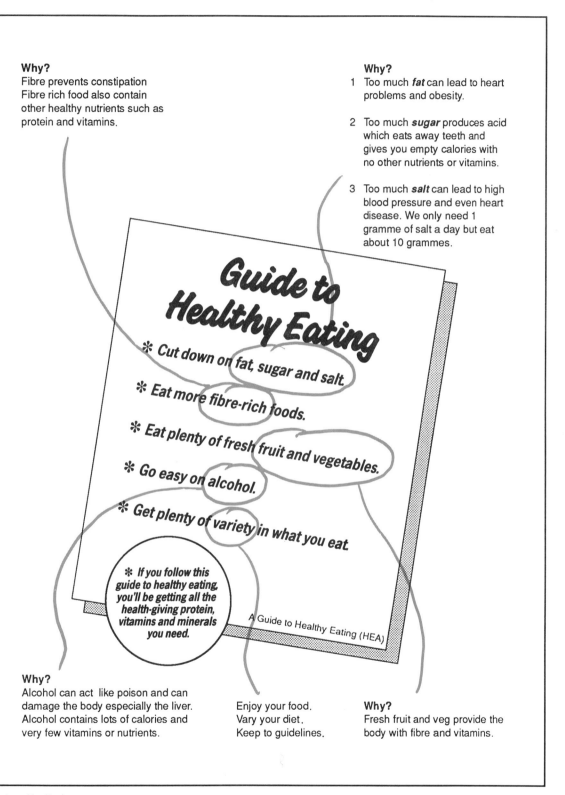

Why?
Fibre prevents constipation
Fibre rich food also contain
other healthy nutrients such as
protein and vitamins.

Why?
1 Too much *fat* can lead to heart
problems and obesity.

2 Too much *sugar* produces acid
which eats away teeth and
gives you empty calories with
no other nutrients or vitamins.

3 Too much *salt* can lead to high
blood pressure and even heart
disease. We only need 1
gramme of salt a day but eat
about 10 grammes.

Guide to Healthy Eating

* Cut down on fat, sugar and salt.

* Eat more fibre-rich foods.

* Eat plenty of fresh fruit and vegetables.

* Go easy on alcohol.

* Get plenty of variety in what you eat

* If you follow this guide to healthy eating, you'll be getting all the health-giving protein, vitamins and minerals you need.

A Guide to Healthy Eating (HEA)

Why?
Alcohol can act like poison and can
damage the body especially the liver.
Alcohol contains lots of calories and
very few vitamins or nutrients.

Enjoy your food.
Vary your diet.
Keep to guidelines.

Why?
Fresh fruit and veg provide the
body with fibre and vitamins.

Extract 1

UNDERSTANDING THE LABEL

They show what the manufacturer has used to produce the food, in order of the amount used. The first ingredient listed is used in the greatest amount, the last one is used in the smallest amount.

Other things to be aware of when reading ingredient lists are pointed out.

BLACK FOREST GATEAU

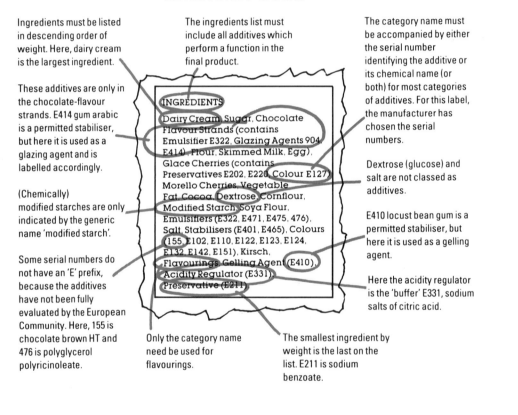

Ingredients must be listed in descending order of weight. Here, dairy cream is the largest ingredient.

These additives are only in the chocolate-flavour strands. E414 gum arabic is a permitted stabiliser, but here it is used as a glazing agent and is labelled accordingly.

(Chemically) modified starches are only indicated by the generic name 'modified starch'.

Some serial numbers do not have an 'E' prefix, because the additives have not been fully evaluated by the European Community. Here, 155 is chocolate brown HT and 476 is polyglycerol polyricinoleate.

The ingredients list must include all additives which perform a function in the final product.

INGREDIENTS
Dairy Cream, Sugar, Chocolate Flavour Strands (contains Emulsifier E322, Glazing Agents 904, E414), Flour, Skimmed Milk, Egg), Glace Cherries (contains Preservatives E202, E220, Colour E127) Morello Cherries, Vegetable Fat, Cocoa, Dextrose, Cornflour, Modified Starch, Soya Flour, Emulsifiers (E322, E471, E475, 476), Salt, Stabilisers (E401, E465), Colours (155, E102, E110, E122, E123, E124, E132, E142, E151), Kirsch, Flavourings Gelling Agent (E410), Acidity Regulator (E331), Preservative (E211)

Only the category name need be used for flavourings.

The category name must be accompanied by either the serial number identifying the additive or its chemical name (or both) for most categories of additives. For this label, the manufacturer has chosen the serial numbers.

Dextrose (glucose) and salt are not classed as additives.

E410 locust bean gum is a permitted stabiliser, but here it is used as a gelling agent.

Here the acidity regulator is the 'buffer' E331, sodium salts of citric acid.

The smallest ingredient by weight is the last on the list. E211 is sodium benzoate.

(Taken from *Food Additives*, published by the Ministry of Agriculture, Fisheries and Food)

(c) Which additives in this gateau do not have an E number? Why not?
(d) What is an E number?
(e) What is E331 made of?

Extract 2

(Taken from *A guide to Health Eating*, published by the Health Education Authority)

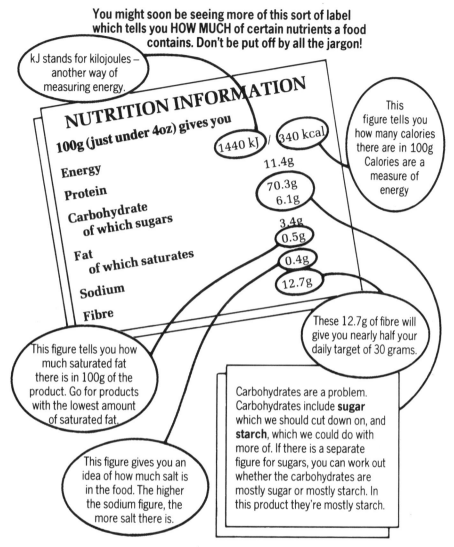

You might soon be seeing more of this sort of label which tells you HOW MUCH of certain nutrients a food contains. Don't be put off by all the jargon!

kJ stands for kilojoules – another way of measuring energy.

NUTRITION INFORMATION
100g (just under 4oz) gives you

Energy   1440 kJ / 340 kcal
Protein   11.4g
Carbohydrate   70.3g
   of which sugars   6.1g
Fat   3.4g
   of which saturates 0.5g
Sodium   0.4g
Fibre   12.7g

This figure tells you how many calories there are in 100g Calories are a measure of energy

These 12.7g of fibre will give you nearly half your daily target of 30 grams.

This figure tells you how much saturated fat there is in 100g of the product. Go for products with the lowest amount of saturated fat.

Carbohydrates are a problem. Carbohydrates include **sugar** which we should cut down on, and **starch**, which we could do with more of. If there is a separate figure for sugars, you can work out whether the carbohydrates are mostly sugar or mostly starch. In this product they're mostly starch.

This figure gives you an idea of how much salt is in the food. The higher the sodium figure, the more salt there is.

2 Read the nutritional information shown above, and answer the following questions.
(*a*) What do kilojoules and calories measure?
(*b*) If 6.1 g of the carbohydrate here is sugar, what does the remainder consist of?
(*c*) What is sodium? Is there a lot or a little of it here?
(*d*) Is this product high or low in fibre?

3 Read closely the tables listing information about four food products and use the information to complete the chart on p 188.

A A breakfast cereal

NUTRITIONAL INFORMATION Per 100g		
Energy	1650 380	kj kcal
Protein	8.0	g

Carbohydrate
  of which sugars   8   g
              starch   76   g
	84	g

Fat of which saturates 0.2 g	0.6	g
Sodium	1.0	g
Fibre	1.0	g

Vitamins:
  Niacin
  Vitamin B_6
  Riboflavin (B_2)
  Thiamin (B_1)
  Folic Acid
  Vitamin D
  Vitamin B_{12}
	
	16
	1.8
	1.5
	1.0
	250
	2.8
	1.7
		
		mg
		mg
		mg
		mg
		μg
		μg
		μg

Iron	6.7	mg

INGREDIENTS: Maize, Sugar, Salt, Malt Flavouring, Niacin, Iron, Vitamin B_6, Riboflavin (B_2), Thiamin (B_1), Folic Acid, Vitamin D, Vitamin B_{12}.

B A packet of biscuits

NUTRITIONAL INFORMATION		
	per 100g	per biscuit
Energy kj	2107	156
kcal	502	37
Fat	24.6g	1.8g
Carbohydrate	64.6g	4.8g
Protein	5.1g	0.4g

INGREDIENTS: Wheatflour, sugar, hydrogenated vegetable oil, chocolate chips (10.0%), hazelnuts (2.1%), dried whey, glucose syrup, raising agents (sodium bicarbonate, ammonium bicarbonate, sodium acid pyrophosphate), salt, carob bean flour, flavouring. To retain freshness once opened, biscuits should be kept in an airtight container.

C A frozen meal

NUTRITIONAL INFORMATION A Typical Example of This Meal Contains	
PROTEIN	33g
FAT	13g
CARBOHYDRATE	40g
ENERGY	1668kj/399k cal

INGREDIENTS: Reconstituted Potato (Water, Dried Potato, Margarine, Salt, Stabiliser (Glycerol Monostearate), Pepper, Nutmeg), Lamb (Minimum 18%), Peas, Gravy (Meat Juices, Water, Gravy Powder), Potato Croquette.

D A tin of soup

Cream of Chicken soup

This soup is made with fine quality ingredients to create a wholesome, nutritious and tasty food. Reflecting today's consumer tastes, the levels of added salt and sugar in our recipes are kept at the minimum possible. This soup is entirely free from artificial colours and preservatives.

NUTRITION INFORMATION		
Typical Values	Amount per 100g	Amount per Serving (212g)
Energy	194kj/46kcal	411kj/98kcal
Protein	1.3g	2.8g
Carbohydrate (of which sugars)	4.5g (0.8g)	9.5g (1.7g)
Fat (of which saturates)	2.7g (0.3g)	5.7g (0.6g)
Sodium	0.4g	0.8g
Dietary Fibre	0.1g	0.2g

INGREDIENTS: Water, Chicken, Flour, Vegetable Oil, Cream, Dried Skimmed Milk, Salt, Cornflour, Modified Cornflour, Flavour Enhancer, Sodium glutamate, Yeast Extract, Emulsifiers, Sodium polyphosphates, Herbs, Spices, Colour – Betacarotene

Food	A	B	C	D
Does the label show ingredients?				
Nutritional analysis?				
How much of the carbohydrate is sugar?				
How much of the fat is saturates?				
Salt content?				
How much fibre the food contains?				
Protein?				
Vitamins?				
Looking at the ingredients, what do you think is the main source of protein?				
What is the main ingredient?				
What is the next ingredient to quantity?				
Does the label follow the HEA guidelines?				

4   Take this book showing the four labels into a local shop or supermarket and compare them with similar products. See if you can find a breakfast cereal, a packet of biscuits, frozen meal and tin of soup that

(i) follows the 'Healthy Eating' advice more closely than the foods these labels came from; and

(ii) is less 'healthy' than the food these labels came from.

Copy down the ingredients and nutritional analysis for each product you select.

TASK 4: HOW HEALTHY IS YOUR DIET?

(*a*) Keep a diary of what you eat and drink for three or four days, including at least part of a weekend, and remember to include snacks and drinks as well as meals. Fill in the information under three headings; 'Day and time'; 'Food/drink' and 'Where/who with'.

(*b*) Analyse your diet in the light of the advice in the (summary) guide on p 183.

• Are you eating a lot of fat, sugar and salt? Have you cut down?

• Are you eating fibre-rich foods – and enough fresh fruit and vegetables?

• Is your alcohol consumption sensible?

• Is there variety in your diet?

(*c*) How much is too much? Find out more precisely.

(i)   How many kilojoules a person of your age, sex and circumstances should consume in a day

(ii) How much fat, sugar, salt, fibre, fruit and veg you should be eating in a day;

(iii) What foods you find these in and in what quantities.

(*d*) (i) Do a detailed analysis of your diet on one day from your diary above. To what extent are you following the advice for healthy eating?

(ii) Suggest changes to your diet that would bring you more in line with advice on healthy eating. Write out a diet sheet for tomorrow, including your changes.

Assignment 20:
Feeding the family

This assignment is concerned with the practicalities of producing good food – i.e. planning, shopping and cooking food that different people with different tastes, needs and backgrounds will enjoy eating. Keep your copy of *A guide to Healthy Eating* to hand. Consider with your tutor what opportunities you will have for practical food preparation in the course of the assignment.

TASK 1:
FAMILY FOOD
DIARIES

Below are the family food diaries kept by two mothers. Study them carefully and discuss the following points with a partner.

(*a*) Look at each meal in turn; breakfast, lunch, dinner, snacks. How healthy is each meal?

(*b*) Look in detail at the differences in eating habits between members of the same family. How do you think these differences arise? What are the consequences for family food planning?

(*c*) To what extent do the diets of these families and the individuals within each family meet the recommendations in the healthy eating guide? First look at the diary a day at a time, then take an overall view.

The Braithwaite family

Both Cheryl and Phil were born in the West Indies and came to this country as young children to join their parents. Cheryl's grandmother also came over, and did much of the cooking in her household when she was growing up. They have two children, Leon, 13, and Maxine 9. Both parents work, Cheryl in a building society and Phil for British Telecom.

The Massini family

Paolo Massini was born and brought up in this country and Bridget O'Leary came over from Ireland when she was 16. Both work; Bridget part time in an old people's home and Paolo manages a shop. They have two children, Marina, 15 and Liam 8.

(*d*) Write a paragraph on the diet on each family, basing your comments on the extent to which you think they meet the five healthy eating points listed on p 183.

THE BRAITHWAITE FAMILY — Food diary (* School dinner)

	Breakfast	Lunch	Snack	Dinner
Sunday				
Cheryl	Mint tea, toast & honey	} Soup, bread & butter	} Bun & cheese	} Rice, black-eyed peas
Phil	Tea, toast & honey			Chicken casserole
Leon	} Orange juice, toast & honey			Rice pudding
Maxine				
Monday				
Cheryl	} Banana porridge } Tea } Orange juice	Cheese roll	Mint tea, biscuit	} Shepherds pie carrots
Phil		Bacon, eggs, chips, tea	————	
Leon		MacDonalds, coke	} Banana, biscuit, tea	Ice cream, tinned fruit
Maxine		*Fish fingers, baked beans cabbage / Sultana sponge & custard		
Tuesday				
Cheryl	} Toast & jam, tea	Cheese roll, apple	Tea, biscuit	
Phil		Bacon sandwich	Kit Kat	} Salt fish, rice, cabbage
Leon	} Cornflakes & milk / Orange juice	Ham roll, crisps, choc. bar	} Bread & jam / Apple juice	Fresh fruit
Maxine		*Cheese flan, mashed potato, mixed veg. / Rhubarb crumble, custard		

THE MASSINI FAMILY — Food diary (* School dinner)

	Breakfast	Lunch	Snack	Dinner
Sunday				
Bridget	} Coffee & toast	Wine } Roast beef, yorkshire pudding, roast potatoes, greens, carrots	Cheese Tea &	on toast biscuits
Paolo				
Marina (15)	Orange juice, yoghourt	Apple crumble & custard (Marina no potatoes)		
Liam (8)	Milk, Shreddies			
Monday				
Bridget	Tea	Ham sandwich	Tea	} Spaghetti bolognese & green salad
Paolo	Coffee, bread & jam	Pizza slice, coke	—	
Marina	Orange juice, toast	Ryvita, cheese, apple, Coke	Biscuit	Fresh fruit
Liam	Shreddies & milk	*Ravioli, mashed potato, beans, sponge pudding	Milk & biscuit	
Tuesday				
Bridget	Tea & toast	(None) Tea		Sausages, onions, mashed potato, cabbage, Ketchup
Paolo	Beans on toast, coffee	Ham roll, coffee		
Marina	Apple juice, cornflakes & milk	*Cheese salad, chocolate bar	Bread & jam	Tea
Liam	Beans on toast, milk	*Chicken pie, mashed potato sweetcorn,	Milk & biscuit	(Cocoa later)

**TASK 2:
ANOTHER FOOD
DIARY**

1 (*a*) Below is another food diary. Study it and comment on how healthy it is, basing your comments again on the five points mentioned above. Consider:
- content of meals;
- frequency of meals;
- what each member of the family eats in the day;
- nutritional needs of the family members.
- extent to which nutritional requirements are being met.

Example page of food diary

**One parent family, London (council flat)
Mother 21 years; three children; Gemma 5 years, Danny 2 years, Terry 11 months**

Time	Food eaten	Quantity	Where eaten	Who by
7.30 am	Tea	1 cup	home	Lorraine & Gemma
	Milk	1 bottle	home	Danny & Terry
8.15 am	Sugar Puffs	1 bowl each	home	All
9.30 am	Tea	1 cup	home	Lorraine
	Warmed milk	1 bottle each	home	Danny & Terry
12 midday	Jam sandwich	1 each	home	Terry & Danny
	Toasted bacon sandwich	1	home	Lorraine
1pm	Peas, potatoes, fish fingers, jelly		school	Gemma
3pm	Tea	1 cup	friend's	Lorraine
	Milk	1 bottle each	friend's	Danny & Terry
5.30 pm	Sausages	2 each	home	L, D & T
	Chips	portion each	home	L, D & T
6.30pm	Tea	1 cup	home	Lorraine
	Milk	1 bottle each	home	Danny & Terry
8.30 pm	Tea	1 cup each	home	Gemma & Lorraine
	Biscuits	4 each	home	Gemma & Lorraine

(Taken from *Diet, Nutrition & Healthy Eating in Low Income Groups*. Published by the Health Education Authority 1989)

(*b*) What factors do you think have shaped this family's diet? Discuss.

(*c*) Plan a practical menu for a day for this family. It must be
- simple to prepare;
- realistic, and acceptable to the family; and
- cheap.

(*d*) Budgeting
  (i) How much would the food you have suggested for the day cost?
  (ii) Assume that this family lives on income support. How much income support would Lorraine receive each week?
  (iii) How much on average do you think Lorraine can afford to spend on food each day? Do your proposals come close to this?

2 (*a*) Follow-up You probably noticed the importance of school dinners in

Gemma's diet. Find out more about school dinners in your area. Topics you might check out include; cost for families that pay; who is eligible for free school dinners; what a typical school dinner consists of; what children actually eat; proportions of children taking a packed lunch and why; constraints on providers of school dinners; provision for minorities.

(b) Present your findings in the form of a written report.

Family favourites

'They don't gear recipes for basic family meals on a low income. The recipes that you see, you have to work them about yourself to put things in and take them out.'

'Every time you cook (from raw ingredients), you've got to buy different things . . . you've got to get the flour, the milk, the butter. I think it's better to get a meat pie from Iceland than cook for yourself.

(Taken from *Diet, Nutrition and 'Healthy Eating' in Low Income Groups,* Health Education Authority 1989)

Everyone who cooks for a family will recognise themselves in these mothers' comments. You do not have to be on a low income to feel annoyed with recipes that would take all day to prepare, use a lot of ingredients you will not find in your cupboard and then the kids will not touch it . . .

Below are some basic family recipes, which are not fiddly, nor expensive; and ingredients can be taken out or added.

Menu 1: Basic mince

You need:
>1lb mince
>1 tin tomatoes
>1 small tin tomato puree or 1 large tin tomato puree
>Salt and pepper to taste

and add
>2 or 3 chopped or grated carrots
>1 onion
>some chopped sticks of celery
>any herbs you like (or none)

What to do: Put a little marg or fat in a frying pan or large saucepan and add the mince. Stir it around to brown. Add the other ingredients. If your frying pan has not got a lid, or it is overful, transfer to a large saucepan. Then add enough water to see it at the top of the mixture. Put a lid or plate over the top to cover, and leave to simmer for about an hour.

The more vegetables you add, the further the mixture will go. You can keep leftovers for at least two days in a fridge, or for as long as you like in a freezer. Work out sizes of margerine tubs that hold portions useful for your family.

You can serve this, a spoonful or two per person, with
- mashed potato (cottage pie)
- rice
- spaghetti or other pasta

You can add
- frozen vegetables to the pasta or rice for the last five minutes or so
- baked beans or a small tin of haricot or kidney beans
- the odd rasher of bacon, chopped small
- grated cheese on top.

Menu 2: Cheese sauce

You need:
1 oz margerine (large spoonful)
1 large rounded tablespoon flour (white or brown)
¼ lb cheese
1 cup milk

What to do: Put the marg in a smallish saucepan over a low gas to melt it. Add flour and stir it in. Let it cook for a minute or so. Then take it off the gas and add a cupful of milk and a cupful of water, stirring all the time. Put the saucepan back on the gas, stirring till it boils. Add grated or chopped cheese. Check the taste.

You can
- use this sauce as it is, with pasta
- stir in frozen or tinned vegetables – spinach, peas, sweetcorn. Stir as it comes back to the boil, and serve with pasta
- serve with any fresh vegetables, e.g. carrots, broccoli, cauliflour, etc. Cook the vegetable with the pasta.
- Add a chopped or mashed hard boiled egg.
- Add a tin of butter beans.

Menu 3: Baked potatoes

An average sized potato takes about an hour to bake, so it needs to go into a medium hot oven (180°C) well before you plan to eat. You can speed this up by boiling for five minutes first.

Aim to serve it with two other accompaniments – something high in protein, and a vegetable, for example
- baked beans and broccoli
- cheese and tomato
- coleslaw and cheese
- sausage and peas or beans

Menu 4: Your family favourite

Add your weekday family favourite to this list. Make sure it is economical and easy to cook and shop for.
   (a) List the ingredients and write clear, easy-to-follow instructions on

how to cook and serve it.

(b) Cost the ingredients, assuming that your 'cupboard items' in List 1 are still there.

TASK 3: PLANNING A MEAL

1 (a) Write a list of ingredients you would need to prepare these meals. Divide your list in two; List 1 of 'cupboard items' you would hope to have in anyway; List 2 of ingredients you would have to buy specially for each meal. Beside each item, note down where you would store it, and how long you could keep it for.

(b) Cost both lists from local shops or a supermarket.

2 **Review:** How is the nutritional value of these meals altered by adding different ingredients to the basic recipe?

TASK 4: PLANNING A MENU FOR THE WEEK

Drawing on all the good food ideas you have come across while you have been doing this assignment, draw up a menu for the week for each household in the six case studies. Your suggestions must be:

- in line with the personal preferences and circumstances of the individuals as far as you can tell;
- sound from a 'healthy eating' point of view;
- meet the particular health and dietary needs of the individuals concerned;
- practical. Liz Hill (CS 5) for example, cannot spend her whole day cooking to meet the different dietary needs of the members of her household; and
- economical and not wasteful. Use everything you put on your shopping list. If you use the outer sticks of celery for the mince, for example, use the inner ones for a salad.

Divide into six groups or pairs for this task. You may need to do some additional research into, for example, how 'healthy eating' guidelines listed on p 183 are modified to take into account the special dietary needs of children and the elderly.

Assignment 21: Mealtime

In this assignment you are asked to think about how food is prepared, served and viewed in institutions that have to cater for large numbers of people.

TASK 1:
ON THE
RECEIVING END

What does it feel like to be incapable of doing something you have done with ease all your life?

These exercises are designed to give you an insight into these feelings.

Note to the tutor: Plan this session carefully. You will need to consider the point in the course to undertake it and it may not be suitable for all groups. Bring the necessary props and equipment and plan the timing of the activities.

1 **Just being.** Divide into four groups. Each group is to experience a different physical limitation.

Group 1: strong rubber bands around fingers
Group 2: arms tied to side with a belt or rope
Group 3: wax ear plugs
Group 4: blindfolds.

When everyone is ready, just sit for a while. Wait for your tutor to ask you to get up and move around. When you have found your way back to your seats, remove your restrictions.

Discuss what it feels like to be handicapped in this way.

2 **Carrying on as usual.** Divide into two groups. The people in Group 1 have a physical restriction, but a different one to the one chosen in **1** above. Group 2's task is to ensure that their partner in Group 1 eats their dinner, helping them as necessary. Today it is:

- Soup
- Semolina or rice pudding
- Tea made in the way the Group 2 person likes it.

The people in Group 2 will measure their success by how much of the dinner gets eaten within the allocated time.

Now change places and tasks with your partner.

3   Discussion points:

(*a*) How did it feel to eat under these circumstances? Draw up a list of words on the board or flipchart to describe your feelings.

(*b*) What were the practical problems with eating in this way? What skills in assisting clients do you think you and your partner need to develop?

(*c*) If this problem you experienced was long term, what effect do you think it might have on your attitudes and behaviour?

4   Write up your experiences in two parts:

Part 1: How you felt eating and drinking in this way

Part 2: How you felt serving food like this.

TASK 2:
A POLICY FOR FOOD
AND HEALTH

Hospitals and residential units now take seriously the feelings of distress you will have experienced in the session above. Many now have a 'Food Policy' based on principles such as:

- a recognition of the importance of 'healthy eating' to health;
- a commitment to educating people in healthier eating habits;
- influencing local catering practices through the purchasing power of a large organisation;

G1	THURSDAY

Please read the information on the back of the Menu Card.

NAME _____

WARD _____ BED No._____

PLEASE INDICATE CHOICE		LUNCH
☐	1	Roast beef, horseradish sauce or
☐	2	Veal fricasse or
☐	3	
☐	4	Chopped pork salad
☐	5	
☐	6	Liver sausage sandwich or
☐	7	Tomato omelette
☐	8	
☐	9	Green salad or
☐	10	Vichy carrots or
☐	11	Brussels sprouts
☐	12	Roast potatoes or
☐	13	Creamed potatoes
☐	14	
☐	15	Jam roly poly and
☐	16	Custard
☐	17	
☐	18	Vanilla ice cream or
☐	19	Fresh fruit or
☐	20	
☐	21	Cheese and biscuits
☐	22	
☐	23	

MENU CHECKED BY MEMBER OF WARD STAFF

SIGNATURE _____

G1	THURSDAY

Please read the information on the back of the **Menu Card.**

NAME _____

WARD _____ BED No._____

PLEASE INDICATE CHOICE		EVENING MEAL
☐	1	Chicken soup
☐	2	
☐	3	
☐	4	Shepherds pie or
☐	5	Mushroom omelette or
☐	6	Chicken for salad or
☐	7	Tuna fish sandwich or
☐	8	Beefburger or
☐	9	Cheese on toast
☐	10	
☐	11	Side salad or
☐	12	Swedes
☐	13	Creamed potatoes
☐	14	
☐	15	
☐	16	
☐	17	Rice pudding or
☐	18	Vanilla ice cream or
☐	19	Fresh fruit or
☐	20	Fruit jelly or
☐	21	Cheese and biscuits
☐	22	
☐	23	

MENU CHECKED BY MEMBER OF WARD STAFF

SIGNATURE _____

Grayswood Hospital Patient Menu

DIET CODES:
R – REDUCING DIET
D – DIABETIC DIET
S – SOFT DIET
V – VEGETARIAN DIET

week 2

Thursday

BREAKFAST

TO INDICATE YOUR CHOICE PLEASE CIRCLE ONE ITEM FROM EACH SECTION BELOW

1. PORRIDGE	DRVS
2. CORNFLAKES	DRV
3. WEETABIX	DRVS
4. RICE KRISPIES	DRV
5. ALLBRAN	DRV
6. BOILED EGG	DRVS

LUNCH

TO INDICATE YOUR CHOICE PLEASE CIRCLE ONE ITEM FROM EACH SECTION BELOW

1. STEAK & KIDNEY PIE	DR
2. CHICKEN CURRY	DRS
3. BAKED POTATO & CHEESE	DRV
4. SCOTCH EGG SALAD	DR

A SELECTION OF VEGETABLES WILL BE SERVED WITH YOUR MEAL

5. APPLE CRUMBLE & CUSTARD	VS
6. STRAWBERRY BLANCMANGE	VS
7. FRUIT COCKTAIL	DRV
8. SPECIAL DIET KOSHER	
9. SPECIAL DIET ETHNIC VEGETARIAN	

PATIENT NAME _____

WARD _____

SUPPER

TO INDICATE YOUR CHOICE PLEASE CIRCLE ONE ITEM FROM EACH SECTION BELOW

1. SCOTCH BROTH	DRS
2. MACARONI CHEESE	DRVS
3. ROAST BEEF SANDWICH	DR

A SELECTION OF VEGETABLES WILL BE SERVED WITH YOUR MEAL

4. CREME CARAMEL	VS
5. FRESH APPLE	DRV
6. ICE CREAM	DRVS
7. CHEESE & BISCUITS	
8. SPECIAL DIET KOSHER	
9. SPECIAL DIET ETHNIC VEGETARIAN	

PATIENT NAME _____

WARD _____

PATIENT NAME _____

WARD _____

- offering the individual consumer greater choice and enjoyment in their food in hospital;
- pricing food in staff canteens so that all staff can afford healthy options;
- offering menus that meet the dietary and cultural needs of all people who eat in the institution.

Draw up a food policy for your college or workplace.

(a) Decide which of the principles above you want to guide your policy. You can use them all, or substitute some new ones of your own.

(b) Decide how to turn these principles into practice. Write each principle as a heading. Under each principle, list three to five practical ways in which you could put the principle into practice in your institution. Add in examples and details where you need to.

TASK 3: YOUR MESSAGE

Design *either* a poster to display in your workplace or college *or* a leaflet to give to staff/students setting out your food policy. You could write a memo to the senior management of the institution enclosing a copy and ask for their comments.

TASK 4: IMPLEMENTING POLICY

You have been asked to analyse the hospital menus on pp 196–7 and to report on

(a) the extent to which they meet 'healthy eating' guidelines

(b) the extent to which they fulfil the principles of the food policy you drew up in Task 2.

Present your findings as a formal report with recommendations.

TASK 5: QUALITY ASSURANCE AT MEALTIME

Opposite is a quality assurance checklist, typical of those in use in long-term hospital or residential settings.

(a) If you have the opportunity to visit a care setting at mealtime, ask the people in charge if you could use the checklist to evaluate the care with which the meal is served. If you do not have this opportunity, redraft these checklist items to include the points you think a good college or workplace canteen should offer. Use your checklist as a basis for an assessment of 'Quality assurance' in your canteen.

(b) Write a paragraph in conclusion in which you summarise your main points and a paragraph of recommendations.

Tables	Yes	No

Do tables have adequate
   Tablecloths
   Condiments
   Napkins
   Glasses
   Water jugs
   Cutlery
   Side plates		

Clients
   Are clients' food preferences recorded in care plans?
   Are clients who should be wearing dentures, wearing them?
Clients sitting at tables, are they
   happy with their companions?
   grouped according to social skills?
   helped to manage their food if necessary?
Clients not at tables, are they
   as upright as possible?
   helped to eat?
Food service
   Were clients offered genuine choice?
   How were clients indicating choice?
   Is hot food served on hot plates?
   Is cold food served on cold plates?
   Does food look appetising and attractive?
   Are portions an appropriate size?
   Were patients offered second helpings?
   Are hot drinks hot?
   Are cold drinks offered?
   Are clients offered sugar and/or milk?
   Are plates removed only when clients have finished?
   Is there a relaxed atmosphere to mealtime?
   Is the food trolley plugged in?
   Are unpopular menu choices reported to Catering Manager?
   Are clients of ethnic minorities and with particular dietary requirements
   offered a menu acceptable to them?
ENVIRONMENT
   Were cleaning activities taking place in or around dining area?
   Was the TV on or off?
   Were staff correctly dressed for serving food?
   Are there any unpleasant and avoidable odours?		

Assignment 22:
Homemaking with Gladys

Background information

Gladys Miller (*see* Case Study 4) moved into 6 Firbank Road, after living in an old mental handicap hospital most of her life. You saw the advertisement on p 259 and applied for a job as Care Assistant in the home. You started work two weeks before Gladys and the other residents moved in. During this time you worked with the occupational therapists in the hospital, getting to know the residents, and accompanied them on visits to Firbank Road. You worked with residents before and after the move, helping them to choose the details and furnishing of their rooms. Below are some of the tasks you have been involved in.

TASK 1: CHOOSING FURNITURE

Shown opposite is a scale drawing of Gladys' room. Your task is to decide how **you** would arrange the following items in the room:
- bed
- easy chair
- bedside table and lamp
- wardrobe or chest of drawers
- small table and upright chair
- rug.

(a) Go out to your local shopping centre with a measuring tape, and find furniture and furnishings you like and you think would be suitable. Note down the dimensions of furniture.

(b) Note down the price of the items you choose. When you come back draw up a 'bill' – a brief description on the left and price on the right. Total up the items. Does the cost surprise you? Have you been extravagant?

(c) Make cut-outs, to scale, of the things you have chosen, and arrange them in the room.

Gladys' room at 6, Firbank Road

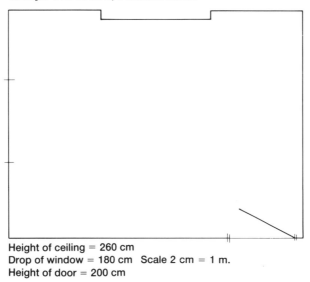

Height of ceiling = 260 cm
Drop of window = 180 cm   Scale 2 cm = 1 m.
Height of door = 200 cm

**TASK 2:
NEGOTIATING
CHANGE**

For this task arrange to work with somebody you have not worked with before in this assignment and who does not know what you have chosen.

Your task is to negotiate with each other, to agree a new arrangement of the items in the room, and a compromise of choice of items. Your aim is that neither of you should 'win' and that you should both feel happy that the outcome reflects your taste and choice.

**TASK 3:
GUIDELINES FOR
COMPROMISE**

1   Feed back to the whole group how you felt having to make changes to your original ideas. Was it easy for you to accept other ideas?

2   If your partner was Gladys, or someone with greater learning difficulties than she has, what practical ways can you suggest for supporting her in the choices **she** makes?

3   To review this discussion, summarise the group's suggestions. Present these in a form you think will be helpful to care assistants new to this work.

**TASK 4:
CHOOSING
CURTAINS**

1   Calculate how much material you would need to make curtains for the window in Gladys' room. Note the following points:
● the finished curtain should be at least the length of the 'drop', or length from the curtain track, to the sill;

- the curtain track extends 10 cm beyond the window on both sides to allow room to clear the window;
- to determine the finished width of each curtain, measure the length of the curtain track and divide by two;
- you need between x1.5 and x2 the finished width of each curtain in material to allow for the gathers, or fullness of the curtain;
- you need to allow 10 cms on each side of each curtain for hemming;
- you need to allow 20 cms on the length for hemming top and bottom.

2 (*a*) When you have worked out how much material you would need, go out to the local shopping centre, choose material and cost it. Then add the cost of thread, curtain tape and lining material if necessary to make a grand total.

(*b*) See if you can find ready made curtains of the correct size in pleasing material and satisfactory quality, and note the cost.

3 If you were helping Gladys to choose curtains, how would you set about it?

Choosing a kettle

**TASK 5:
SPOTTING THE
DETAILS**

Study the details of the kettles opposite and complete the chart below.

Details of kettle	Kettle no: 1	2	3	4
Type J (jug) R (round)				
Automatic switch off (Y/N)				
Flex plugs into K (kettle) or B (base)				
Water level indicator (Y/N)				
On-light (Y/N)				
Maximum capacity				
Wattage				
Other special features				
Price				

**TASK 6:
A KETTLE
FOR GLADYS**

Your supervisor in Firbank Road leaves you this note

The kettle they sent down must be 20 years old if it's a day! I think we should get a new one for the kitchen. Could you have a look in the catalogue and pick out a model you think would be suitable – safe and easy for the residents to use. We can get it immediately if it's under £20. Could you let me know which one you decide on and why?

Decide which kettle you think you should buy and write a memo to Mrs Jardine with the information as she asked for. For memo layout, *see* p 274.

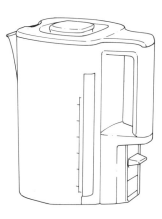

1. CORDLESS AUTOMATIC
KETTLES. Water level indicator. Just lift
kettle to disconnect from base for
pouring and filling. Neon on-light.
Maximum capacity 3 pint. 2200 watt.
　Brown/Beige.
Cat. No.
014/0603　　　　　　　　£21.25

2. AUTOMATIC KETTLE.
Water level indicator.
Maximum capacity 3 pint. 2200 watt.
Cat. No.
014/9011　　　　　　　　£13.95

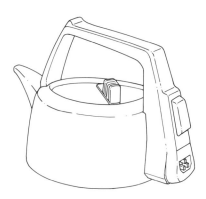

3. 3 PINT AUTOMATIC KETTLE.
Stainless steel body. 2200 watt.
Cat. No.
014/2319　　　　　　　　£21.25

4. CORDLESS AUTOMATIC
KETTLE. Grey/white. Just lift kettle to
disconnect from base for pouring and
filling. Cord storage with 3 cord outlet
positions. Neon on-light. Maximum
capacity 3 pint. 2200 watt.
Cat. No.
014/0011　　　　　　　　£21.25

TASK 7: Complete the order form shown below for the kettle you chose.
PLACING AN ORDER

CUSTOMER SELECTION FORM

CATALOGUE NUMBER								QTY	SHOWROOM USE ONLY	
EXAMPLE										
1	2	3		4	5	6	7	1		
SHOWROOM USE ONLY										
Cash	Chq	Access Card	Amex Card		Diners Card	Visa Card	Prom. Vouch.	Gift Vouch.		

CHECK OUT THE IN-STORE CATALOGUE FOR MANY MORE OFFERS AND THE LATEST NEW PRODUCTS

Assignment 23:
Planning a future

This assignment is a follow-up to Case Study 2 about Andrew Neale. Before you tackle this assignment, re-read the case study on p 43 and your assessment on p 45.

In September, three and a half years after his accident, Andrew's compensation money came through. It seemed a dazzling sum, but by the time he and his dad started finding out how much everything cost, Andy could see that he would need to be careful to ensure that the money went as far as possible.

TASK 1:
A HOLIDAY FOR MR
AND MRS NEALE

When Andrew had his accident, his parents had to cancel their holiday, and they had not had a break since. Andrew is determined that they should have a holiday now.

Go to a travel agent, collect some holiday brochures and find two reasonably priced one-week holidays from which Andrew could choose a surprise holiday for his parents. First agree on a price limit.

Note: Mr and Mrs Neale like sunshine, but not too much heat (not above the high 70s). They like small family-run hotels, not big tower blocks, and they do not like noisy resorts. They like a swimming pool. Mrs Neale does not like foreign cooking, but Mr Neale does.

TASK 2:
A HOLIDAY
FOR ANDY?

Andrew would like to go on holiday himself. Steve has agreed to come with him. Choose two holiday options you could offer to Andy. Present the details of your choices, and explain why you think they would be suitable for Andy and Steve.

1   Find out the names and addresses of two organisations that offer holidays for people with physical disabilities. Write a letter to each, asking for them to send you details of their holidays. You may want to explain that this is part of your coursework, or you may decide to ask about holidays for young people with a physical disability such as Andy.

2 Go to an ordinary travel agent. Find out which holidays might be suitable for Andy and Steve.

Note: With well designed and accessible facilities, Andy can be independent in personal care. Steve will help him get out and about, but Andrew does not want him to have to help with intimate tasks. Remember to take into account the practicalities of travel as well as the location itself.

Andy's place

Andy lost no time in contacting all the people who could offer him help in his determination to get a place of his own. The council and housing association were sympathetic to his needs, but had had their budgets cut drastically so Andy would be at the end of a long waiting list of people with higher priority. Andy decided to look for a place to buy with his compensation money and pay for the renovations and adaptations himself with whatever grants he could obtain. The housing association put him in touch with an architect who had done a lot of conversions for them in the past. The social services occupational therapist, district council building surveyor and environmental health officer were all incredibly helpful. (You may like to check with the diagram of the structure of a local authority on p 23 to see where they all fit in.)

Andy found a ground floor flat in an end of terrace Victorian house in need of renovation near the centre of town. 18 months later . . .

TASK 3:
BEFORE AND AFTER

Study the plans carefully and notice the differences before and after the adaptations were carried out.

(*a*) Working in pairs, take it in turns to point out to your partner one 'before and after' change and explain what you think is the reason for the change. See how many you can spot.

(*b*) Six changes are numbered on both plans. Answer the following questions;

(1) What is the difference here? Why has this been done?

(2) Why has the under stairs cupboard been cut back?

(3) How wide were these doorways? How wide are they now? Why has this been done? What is different about the type of door?

(4) How have these rooms been changed? Why?

(5) What sort of door is this? What is the difference?

(6) What major changes have been made to the kitchen?

(*c*) Imagine you have just entered Andy's sitting room. Describe the layout and furnishing of the room as you would see it from the door.

TASK 4:
THINKING ABOUT
DESIGN

Read Task 5 before you start.
Find out about design considerations for people with physical disabilities. Think of Andy's particular needs as you look. You can try:

• the local library, probably the reference section;

Andy's flat before adaptation

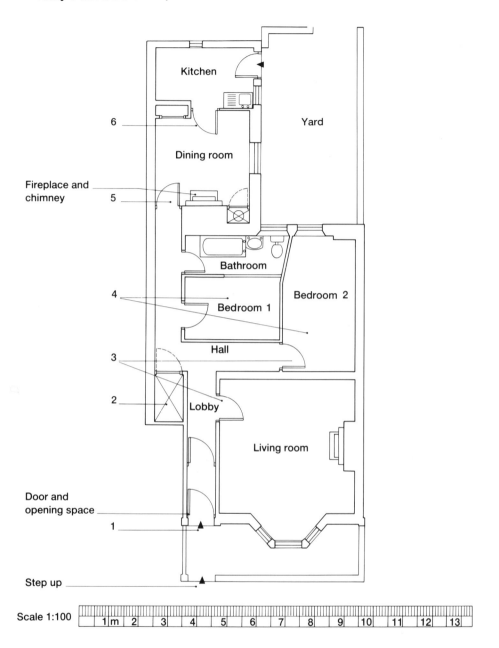

Ground floor plan before adaptation.
1:100

Andy's flat after adaptation

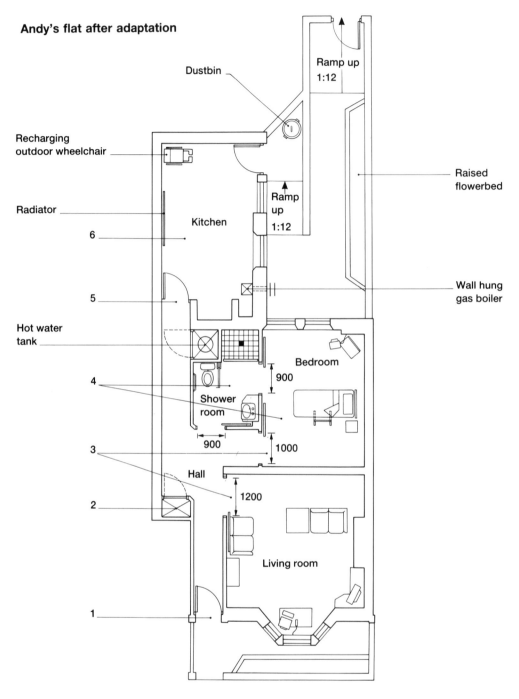

Dustbin

Ramp up
1:12

Recharging
outdoor wheelchair

Raised
flowerbed

Radiator

Kitchen

6

Ramp
up
1:12

5

Wall hung
gas boiler

Hot water
tank

Bedroom

900

4

Shower
room

900

1000

3

Hall

2

1200

1

Living room

Ground floor plan
after adaptation. 1:100

(The plans on 207 and above have been adapted from *House
Adaptions for People with Physical Disabilities* by R Statham,
J Korczak & P Monoghan, HMSO 1988)

- a specialist medical or nursing library;
- organisations that specialise in designing for people with disabilities, such as the Disabled Living Foundation, Spastics Society. You may be able to visit an exhibition.
- the occupational therapist in your local social services department.

TASK 5: DESIGN THE KITCHEN

You have probably noticed that no equipment or furniture is marked in the kitchen. This is for you to do.

1 (*a*) Make a 1:25 scale drawing of the kitchen after conversion on graph paper. Draw the shape accurately and mark in the fixed features.

(*b*) Think about and decide the following:

- What would be a convenient height for the work surfaces for Andy?
- How can he get close enough to them in a wheelchair?
- How much space does he need to turn his wheelchair with ease?

(*c*) Decide on the most convenient design and position for the following; sink, cooker, electric kettle, toaster, fridge/freezer, storage for pots and pans, crockery, food.

(*d*) Make a neat and accurate drawing of your layout.

2 **Follow-up.** What grants for house adaptations could Andy get? What benefits is he eligible for?

Assignment 24:
Warm and well

This assignment looks at the effect of cold weather on the people's health and general well being. Elderly people and small babies are particularly vulnerable to the cold, but it affects everyone – we all make some preparation for the approach of winter.

**TASK 1:
COLD WEATHER
AND YOU**

1   Discussion points:
   (*a*) How do you feel about the approach of colder weather?
   (*b*) What preparations do you make for wintry weather?
   (*c*) What difference does cold weather make to your way of life?
   (*d*) What is the difference between what you spend money on in summer and winter? When do you spend more money?

2   How do you think each of the people in the case studies would answer the questions you have just discussed? Work in six groups for this, taking a case study each.

   In your report back to the whole group, highlight
   (*a*) the different ways in which each person is affected.
   (*b*) any needs your person may have that you think they will be unable to deal with unaided.

**TASK 2:
FOOD IS FUEL**

'The right food and drink are vitally important to keeping warm and healthy in the long winter days. During cold weather, hot meals and plenty of hot drinks will make you feel warmer inside . . . A warm drink before going to bed may help to keep you warm.'

1   Your task here is to put this advice into practice. Do either (*a*) or (*b*).
   (*a*) In Task 4 in Assignment 20 you drew up menus for each household in the Case Studies. What changes could you make in cold winter weather to the diets you suggested here?
   (*b*) Suggest a hot and healthy breakfast and two hot snacks during the day that you think might be acceptable to each Case Study household.

2   What additional cost do your suggestions involve?

**TASK 3:
WRAPPING
UP WARM**

1   Below are some tips for keeping warm. List them down the lefthand side of your page, and add an explanation for each tip on the right.

- Keep active
- Wear several layers of clothing, rather than one thick layer
- Natural fibres are warmer than most synthetic ones
- Wear a hat, gloves and scarf outside
- Use hot water bottles
- Keep one room well heated

2   Gladys, in Case Study 4, has seen a jumper she likes in a catalogue. She has asked you to help her order it. Do this task in pairs, and take it in turns to be Gladys. Choose a colour from the description below and invent any additional information needed. The second person should ask for these details and complete the form on p 212.

TURTLE NECK SWEATER

OUR TURTLE *neck sweater has the wonderfully soft feel of angora, partially mixed with lambswool. It looks great under suit jackets, sporty separates and casual clothes. This sweater is fully fashioned through the shoulderline and includes soft shoulder pads. 70% lambswool, 20% angora, 10% nylon. Washable.*
Pink Sweater
216 07Z 126
Ivory Sweater
216 08Z 126
Black Sweater
216 09Z 126
Sizes 10 12/14 16/18

£19.99

**TASK 4:
KEEPING THE
HOUSE WARM**

Look at the Fuel Saving Tips from the leaflet, 'Warmth in Winter' on p 213.
1   In pairs, phone or visit a hardware shop and find out the cost of the improvements for doors and windows suggested in the leaflet.
2   Which other suggestions do you think an elderly person should try? Do you have any to add?
3   Calculate the total cost of making these improvements to the ground floor of a home. Do you think this is a reasonable amount for a person on a state pension to pay?

ORDER FORM

Complete in BLOCK capitals please.

Title Mr/Mrs/Miss   Initials   Surname   Tel. no. in case of queries

Address (Please Print)

Town | Please enter postcode to ensure speedy delivery | Postcode

Delivery address if different from above

Town | Please enter postcode to ensure speedy delivery | Postcode

total

Catalogue Number	Product Description	Size	Colour	£ Price each p	Qty.	£ Total each p

Handling and Delivery Charge. Please enter for **1 item £1.99**, for **2 items £2.80**, for **3 more items £3.50**

TOTAL

Handling and Delivery Charge

GRAND TOTAL

Please select your method of payment and complete the relevant details below:

I enclose a cheque/postal order for: £   Ref. No.   **C6201**

month   year

Expiry Date:

I wish to pay by
Visa/Mastercard/Access/
Diners Club/Amex/Next

I wish to pay over the period of time indicated
SEND NO MONEY NOW (please tick as appropriate)

4 months   12 months

My credit card number is

SIGNED   (I am over 18 years of age)   DATE

We reserve the right to refuse your order. Delivery subject to availability. UK only including C.I.

(Reproduced by kind permission of the Health Education Authority)

FUEL SAVING TIPS

Your home can lose a lot of heat through draughts. These can be treated.

BUT ALWAYS REMEMBER TO LEAVE ENOUGH VENTILATION FOR GAS AND COAL FIRES, AND NEVER TO BLOCK VENTILATION BRICKS.

Hardware shops and department stores usually sell materials for draughtproofing.

Doors

You can:

- put metal, plastic or foam strips around the sides of doors
- fit draught excluders to the bottoms of doors
- get special covers for letterboxes
- hang a heavy curtain over the front door to make the hall warmer

Windows

- If your windows don't fit properly, you can lose a lot of heat. So seal gaps in window frames and between frames and walls.
- Double glazing is very expensive. It's much cheaper to attach plastic sheeting to windows by a wooden frame, double-sided tape, or magnetic strip, but make sure that this is easily detachable in case of fire.
- Have heavy curtains or curtains with thermal linings.

more FUEL SAVING TIPS

There are many other things you can do to cut your fuel costs. For example:

- cook a complete meal in the oven all at once
- use a bowl instead of running hot water for washing your hands or dishes, and rinse dishes in cold water.

If you have central heating:

- let the room thermostat control the temperature. Don't use it as a switch. Turning up the thermostat won't heat the room faster. Turn up the boiler instead but don't forget that this will use more fuel.
- if the room gets too hot, don't open the windows. Turn down the thermostat instead.
- have your boiler serviced once a year, or at least every two years.
- put kitchen foil, shiny side out, behind the radiators on outside walls to reflect heat.
- fix small shelves above radiators to push warm air towards the centre of the room.

You can get advice on how to make the most of your heating system. Ask at your local gas or electricity showroom.

SAFETY

Put guards on all fires, and don't get too close.
Don't put clothes on heaters.

TASK 5: COUNTING THE COST

Shown on p 214 is an extract from an electricity board leaflet. Read it carefully and answer the questions below.

(a) How many watts are there in a kilowatt?

(b) How long would 150 watt light take to use up a unit?

(c) How long would a two kilowatt fire take to use up a unit?

(d) Which of these heaters is cheapest to run; convector, fan, infra-red, oil-filled radiator, panel, radiant? Which is the most expensive?

(e) Suppose electricity costs seven pence a unit. How much would (i) the storage heater, and (ii) the hot water tank shown here cost to run per week, using the sample figures supplied?

A GUIDE TO RUNNING COSTS

Just as food is sold by the pound or kilogram so electricity is sold by the unit. One unit of electricity is used at the rate of one kilowatt (1 kW) or 1000 watts for one hour. This means that for one unit a 100 watt (100 W) lamp will light continuously for 10 hours and a 1000 W (1 kW) electric fire will give off heat for one hour.

Look what you get for one or more units!

Heaters

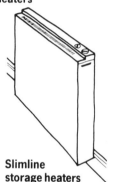

Slimline storage heaters
Use Economy 7 low cost night rate electricity. Depending on the level of thermal insulation in the home, a 2kW model uses an average of 45 to 75 units per week during the heating season. Larger models use proportionately more.

Convector heater (2kW)
½ hour's warmth for 1 unit

Fan heater (2kW)
½ hour's warmth for 1 unit

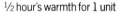

Infra-red heater (1kW)
1 hour's warmth for 1 unit
Oil-filled radiator (500W)
2 hours' warmth for 1 unit
Panel heater (1.5kW)
40 minutes' warmth for 1 unit
Radiant heater (3kW)
20 minutes' warmth for 1 unit
Heating pad (30W)
More than 30 hours' operation for 1 unit

Kettle
12 pints of boiling water for 1 unit

Hot water

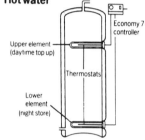

Economy 7 controller

Upper element (daytime top up)

Thermostats

Lower element (night store)

Using a high-performance factory-insulated 210 litre (46 gallon) Economy 7 cylinder with two side entry heaters: hot water for a family of four – 67 units per week
Over 90% of these units can be used at the cheap night rate on the Economy 7 tariff.

Instant water heater
More than 3 gallons of piping hot water for 1 unit

Iron
1 hour's use for ½ to 1 unit

(*f*) If you used the capacity of the instant water heater ten times in a day, how much would your hot water cost for a week? How much would your electricity for this alone cost over a quarter?

(*g*) If the capacity of the kettle shown is three pints, how many full kettlefuls can you boil for the price of a unit?

(*h*) Look at the kettles shown on p 203. Are some more expensive to run than others?

Hypothermia

The normal, healthy, body temperature is 98.4°F or 37°C.

People at risk in cold weather are likely to be:

Either people over pension age – and the older you are, the more at risk you are;

or people with disabilities – particularly if your disability affects your mobility;

or if you have an illness such as diabetes, sickle cell anaemia, thalassaemia, heart disease, circulation problems, etc.;

or if your disability affects how you communicate, eg. if you are deaf, confused, etc.

It's well known that many more people die in winter and spring than in summer and autumn. Most of the increased mortality rate however, is not the result of hypothermia but 'minor' ailments exacerbated by the cold. Being at risk when it's cold means either that your body can't keep itself warm enough – which eventually leads to becoming hypothermic – or that when your blood thickens, which it does when it gets cold, it can't circulate properly – so be careful if you've got weak heart.

What is hypothermia?

Hypothermia is a possibility if someone who is obviously cold:

- Doesn't feel the cold
- Is confused and drowsy
- Has slurred speech
- Feels cold to the touch, especially armpits, abdomen, between thighs.
- Feels stiff
- Breathes slowly and shallowly.
- Has a puffy face.
- A black person might have a pale or ashen grey face.
- A white person might have a chalky pale or flushed face.

If you think that you, or someone you know, might be hypothermic:

- Send for medical assistance.
- Warm up the room but *don't direct the heat at the person*
- Warm up the person with *lightweight* blankets or clothes (weight interferes with blood circulation and gives less insulation);
- If the person is fully conscious, give *warm* (not hot) drinks.

DO NOT.

- Give any alcohol
- Use hot water bottles

- Put the person in a hot bath.
- Put the person near a fire or heater.

(Taken from the Age Concern Hackney Handbook)

TASK 6:
SPREADING
THE MESSAGE

In small groups prepare a **one minute** advert for local radio which would alert vulnerable people and their carers to:
- signs of hypothermia and other cold related illnesses;
- ways of coping with the cold; and
- agencies who can help.

Plan of action
1 **Research** your topic. Try library, tutor, supervisor
2 **Plan** advert. Decide on your essential message, and how to put it across.
3 **Write** script; include voices, sound effects.
4 **Rehearse** – make changes
5 **Rehearse** again
6 **Tape** the broadcast

Assignment 25:
Going home

Mrs Taylor, (*see* Case Study 6) has made a good recovery after her admission to hospital (*see* Assignment 31). She stayed a week on the general medical ward and she was then transferred to a geriatric ward where she has been for nearly two weeks. Movement was painful and her right arm in particular was badly bruised and is still weak. She is frail and her balance was affected but now she is feeling much steadier and more confident on her feet. She has had a visitor most days; her family and Mrs O'Brien have all been, but she is now looking forward to going home.

The staff have been discussing her discharge with her for some time. Mrs Taylor is confident that she will manage fine with a bit of extra help especially in the first few weeks. Her discharge is planned for next Tuesday.

How does the hospital ensure that she does not go back to an empty house?

1   The medical staff write a discharge letter to her GP who will visit her when she gets home. Meanwhile he has contacted the District Nurse, who plans to pop in to see her in hospital before she leaves.

2   The hospital social worker has contacted Social Services. A social worker will visit Mrs Taylor to make an assessment of her needs for domiciliary support.

3   That leaves the practical details. Who will take her home? Warm up the house? Get some food in? The staff talk to Mrs Taylor's family.

TASK 1:
THINKING
IT THROUGH

Mrs Taylor is fortunate in having quite a lot of support at home; a willing family, Mrs O'Brien, good neighbours. But she will still have needs . . .

1   What services will the social worker be thinking about when she visits? For each service you identify decide (*a*) whether Mrs Taylor needs it; and (*b*) whether she would be eligible for it.

2   Look at the article 'Help from Home' on p 18. Find out if such a scheme operates in your area, and if so, who is accepted for it.

K95 SPILLNOT
Moulded in a creamy white A.B.S. plastic, this clever design has three sunken areas of different diameters in the form of inverted cones, lined with a non-slip material.
Jars or bottles when placed into the appropriate cone are gripped firmly by the sides leaving both hands free for opening the container. Non-slip feet stop it sliding around the work top.

K34 'RED CLARA' TIN OPENER
A very sturdy opener, moulded in a white A.B.S. plastic, which may be hand held or wall mounted. With a large grip handle and a simple positive cutting action it has been found in independent tests to be the easiest opener to operate for people with a weak grip.

K23 TEA POT TIPPER
This wooden-framed tipper has a melamine faced platform fitted with rubber blocks angled to stop the tea pot sliding.
Non-slip feet hold the tipper firmly on the work surface. The handle of the tea pot should be used for tipping, not the platform.
Dimensions 8¼″ (210mm) x 7¼″ (185mm) x 4″ (105mm)

K62 MINI SIEGER
A hand held opener working on a similar principle to the Undoit (K11) but smaller. Opens tops from ¾″ (20mm) to 1½″ (40mm).

K28 STRONGBOY
A flexible stainless steel band at one end of a plastic handle may be tightened or loosened by means of a screw at the other end. When clamped round a jar lid, considerable leverage may be obtained to break that stubborn seal.
It can be used in conjunction with the Spillnot (K95).
Suitable for tops from ¾″ (20mm) to 4⅓″ (110mm) diameter.

K93 SIEGER BOY TIN OPENER
One handed.

A popular hand held opener with a large moulded turning handle for maximum grip. It may be used one handed in conjunction with a holding device such as the Belliclamp or Spillnot

K11 UNDOIT OPENER
The V shaped steel opener has a black non-slip insert. It is screwed to the underside of a shelf and jar tops slid into its jaws until wedged tight. Both hands are then free to twist the jar. Suitable for jar tops from 1″ (25mm) to 3″ (75mm)

K98 SCREW TOP OPENER
A simple but effective screw grip for the tops of mineral or soft drink type bottles. It also has a crown cap opener at the other end.

DYCEM

Dycem has been developed from P.V.C., by a patent method, to produce by far the most effective non-slip material on the market. It is not sticky and provides a gripping surface on both sides which makes it ideal for use wherever a dry slippery surface presents a problem — work tops, polished furniture or floors, trays etc. It may also be used in the hand to enhance the grip when opening jars.

K116 etc. DYCEM GRIPPIMATS
Individual mats cut from Dycem sheet. Sold in sets of three except K149 Tray Mat.

K116	7½″ (190mm) Round Mat (Set of 3)	
K118	9½″ (240mm) x 7½″ (90mm) (Set of 3)	
K149	Traymat 15″ (375mm) x 11″ (275mm) (Single Only)	

Available in red, blue, beige or white.

K148	Traymat Patterned 15″ (375mm) x 11″ (275mm) (Single Only)	

3   Mrs Taylor has a follow-up outpatients appointment in a month's time. How will she get there?

TASK 2:
NOT AN
EMPTY HOUSE

1   List the tasks that you think need to be done to prepare an elderly person's home for their return from hospital in November.
2   Draw up a menu for Mrs Taylor for the first week after her return from hospital. Draw on the suggestions in Assignments 19 and 24. Make full use of Mrs O'Brien's two mornings a week. If you decide that Mrs Taylor is entitled to receive meals-on-wheels, take this into account in your planning.
3   Draw up a shopping list for the week's food and cost it.

TASK 3:
STAYING
INDEPENDENT

Mrs Taylor is pleased to be home but her inability to do some things worries her. Her right arm is still very weak, and tires quickly. She has to use both hands to lift the kettle, teapot and saucepans. Her arm aches even when she holds the saucepan with her right hand and stirs with her left, and her grip on vegetables is weak. With only one hand, plates, pans and potatoes tend to slide and slip . . . She worries that she will forget to ask Mrs O'Brien to open any tins she may want. Stiff lids defeat her – and so do easier ones. The bathroom also worries her. She finds it hard to get a grip on the slippery sides, lower herself down and raise herself out . . .
1   Shown opposite is a selection of kitchen equipment from a specialist catalogue.
     (a) Decide what you think Mrs Taylor's needs are and which of the items shown would be most useful to her.
     (b) Make your selection, find out the price of each item you choose from the price list and complete the order form on pp 220–1.
2   Mrs Taylor is also worried about the bathroom. Find out about equipment she might find helpful. Choose two or three items, explain their use, and cost them.

HOMECRAFT WHOLESALE PRICE LIST

	CODE	PRODUCT DESCRIPTION	
	K1	Dustpan and Brush — Long-Handled	3.87
	K2F	Egg Cup with Suction Base — Red	0.70
	K21	Egg Cup with Suction Base — Yellow	0.70
	K3	Magic Broom Lightweight Vacuum Cleaner	34.44
	K10	Pat Saunders One-way Straw (pair)	1.59
	K11	Undo-it Under-shelf Jar & Bottle Opener	1.51
	K12	Open-all Jar & Bottle Opener	1.48
	K13	Croydon Tin Opener and Stand	12.86
	K14	Tin Stand — Wall-Mounting	5.84
	K15	Etwall Standard Trolley — 900 mm High	41.05
	K15D	Etwall Dining Trolley — 835 mm High	42.05
	K15F	Economy Standard Trolley Flatpack — 900 mm	39.45
	K15L	Etwall Standard Trolley — 810 mm High	41.05
	K18	Crystal Tap Turner	6.88
	K20	Homecraft Tap Turner	2.35
	K21	Suregrip Stand with Suction Feet	1.44
	K22	Bread Board	5.95
	K22A	Buttering Board	2.25
	K23	Teapot Pourer and Stand	7.25
	K24	Tapturn Tap Turners — Red and Blue Pair	2.55
	K25	Bottle Holder — Long-Handled	5.45
	K25W	Bottle Holder — Wall-Mounted	3.00
	K26	Cooking Basket	4.03
	K27	Ritter Peeler — Plastic	0.91
	K28	Strongboy Jar & Bottle Opener	4.25
	K29	One-Handed Whisk	2.79
	K30	Milk Saver	1.60
	K31	Clyde Grater/Scraper	8.61
	K31A	Spike Set Attachment for Clyde Grater	1.29
	K32	Gordon Peeler with Clamp	7.59
	K33	Rex Peeler — Metal	1.09
	K34	Red Clara Tin Opener — Wall-Mounted	6.95
R	K34A	To be Deleted when Stocks Exhausted	8.29
	K35	Contour Turner	5.11
	K36	Twister Jar Opener	1.59
	K37	Sherwood Kitchen Stool 610 mm — Standard	19.76
	K37L	Sherwood Kitchen Stool 535 mm — Low	19.76
	K38	Small Plate Surround	2.40
	K39	Slitapac Opener — Wall-mounted	1.09
	K60	Incurve Plate Surround	2.15
	K62	Mini-Sieger Screw-Cap Bottle Opener	1.90
	K63	Two Handled Mug	1.23
	K80	Selectagrip Small Grip Handle	0.65
	K81	Selectagrip Large Grip Handle	0.96
	K82	Selectagrip Oval Handle	0.86
	K83	Selectagrip Hand Strap for K89 Handle	0.86
	K84	Selectagrip Multi-Strap — 1 Metre	0.99
	K89	Selectagrip Standard Grip Handle	0.39
	K90	Philips Tin Opener — Mains Powered	12.95
	K90A	Philips Tin Opener and Handiplug	14.95
R	K92	To be Replaced by K105	19.68
R	K92A	To be Replaced by K105A	21.68
	K93	Sieger Boy Tin Opener	7.15
	K94	Tin Opener — Right or Left Handed	3.75
	K95	Spillnot Jar and Bottle Holder	9.05
	K96	Magi-Twist Jar Opener	4.54
N	K97	Screw-Top Bottle Opener/Knob Turner	1.95
	K98	Screw-Cap and Crown-Cap Bottle Opener	1.32
	K99	Walsall Trolley	49.95
	K100	Belliclamp Jar and Bottle Holder	11.45
	K118A	Dycem Grippimats 240 x 190 mm — White x 3	3.30
	K118B	Dycem Grippimats 240 x 190 mm — Blue x 3	3.30
	K118F	Dycem Grippimats 240 x 190 mm — Red x 3	3.30
	K118H	Dycem Grippimats 240 x 190 mm — Beige x 3	3.30
	K139	Sherwood Kitchen Stool with Back/Armrest	30.96
	K140	Freehand Tray with Dycem Non-Slip Mat	15.70
	K141	Tray with Dycem Non-Slip Mat	7.46
	K142	Tray with Dycem Coating — Country Design	9.63
R	K143	To be Deleted when Stocks Exhausted	4.59

Operation Homehelp from	*Homecraft*	**HOMECRAFT SUPPLIES LIMITED** Low Moor Estate, Kirkby-in-Ashfield, Notts. NG17 7JZ. Tel: 0623 757955 V.A.T. Reg No. 218-0755-70 Date of Order			

QUANTITY	ITEMS REQUIRED	PRODUCT CODE	PRICES FROM CURRENT LIST	TOTAL PRICE £ p	OFFICE USE
	TOTAL VALUE EXCLUSIVE OF CARRIAGE AND PACKAGING				
	CARRIAGE AND PACKAGING AT 10% OF ORDER VALUE WITH £0.50 MINIMUM CHARGE AND £3.00 MAXIMUM CHARGE				
	TOTAL PAYABLE TO HOMECRAFT SUPPLIES LTD.				

EXPIRY DATE OF CREDIT CARD ....   PLEASE TICK PAYMENT METHOD

ACCESS ☐   VISA ☐   CHEQUE ☐   POSTAL ORDER ☐

CARD NO. ☐☐☐☐☐☐☐☐☐☐☐☐☐☐   SIGNATURE ....

NAME & ADDRESS OF CREDIT CARD HOLDER ....
....

TASK 4:
THE ELECTRICITY BILL

In December Mrs Taylor receives a Final Notice from the Electricity Board. She is very distressed and puzzled – she had been in hospital most of November and this bill is far more than her winter bills usually are. She tried to ring herself but failed to get an answer. She asks you to write to the electricity board for her.

1 (a) Write to the electricity board. First decide what points you want to make. You decide to enclose a reading of her meter, on a form you collected from the showroom, shown on p 222. Complete it, taking the reading from your meter at home. The leaflet explains how to do it. Use the address of your own electricity board and refer to 'How to set out letters' on p 276 for letter layout.
(b) Write the reply you hope Mrs Taylor would receive from the electricity board.

2 What organisations can offer help or advice to elderly people during a cold spell? In pairs contact one of these organisations and ask them to send you information. Display this in a form accessible to the whole group.

An example (fictitious) of a
Final Notice sent by an
electricity board.

London Electricity

CUSTOMER SERVICES OFFICE	DATE
1 CITY ROAD LONDON E24 2NO	5/12/9–

WHEN TELEPHONING
We have a call queuing
system. When you hear
the ringing tone please
wait for a reply as calls
are answered in strict
rotation.

Please ignore this notice
if you have already paid
your bill.

Mrs N Taylor
59 Church Street
Wendleford
LONDON
SW21 7PQ

FINAL NOTICE

Our records show that you have still not paid your electricity bill. Payment
for the electricity used was due at the time you received that bill.

To stop us having to take further action please pay the outstanding amount
immediately.

If we do not receive payment within SEVEN DAYS we may have to cut off
your supply and an extra charge would then be payable to have it put back
on. A security deposit may also be required.

HAVING DIFFICULTY PAYING?

Then turn the page to find out how we can help.
Please do not ignore this letter as further action will result.

YOUR ACCOUNT NUMBER	YOU CAN PHONE US ON		AMOUNT TO PAY
047.4332/008.932	071–870 3099		227.25

Form No. 1.128/1A 0490

PLEASE COMPLETE THIS FULLY

NAME _____ SHOWROOM _____

ADDRESS _____

ACCOUNT REFERENCE _____ METER NO. (last 5 digits) _____

DIAL METER

Check the first dial to see if the '9' is to the right
or left of the '0'
If it is on the right, copy the position of the
pointers on this set of dials →

| 10,000 | 1,000 | 100 | 10 | 1 |

If it is on the left, copy the position of the pointers on
this set of dials →
PLEASE IGNORE ALL RED DIALS/NUMBERS

| 10,000 | 1,000 | 100 | 10 | 1 |

NON DIAL METER	10,000	1,000	100	10	1 (kWh)
enter readings here →					

TWO-RATE METER	LOW			
enter readings here →	NORMAL			

Dial meter

Reading this type of meter is more complicated, but after a little practice you'll find it quite straightforward.

When reading your dial meter, always remember that adjacent dials revolve in opposite directions. Ignore the dial marked $\frac{1}{10}$ (it's only there for testing purposes) and read the other five dials from **left to right.**

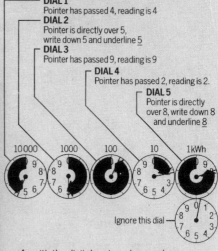

adjusting to eliminate small variations in the pointer positions.

d) Look at the figures <u>underlined.</u> If one of these is followed by a 9, reduce the underlined figure by 1.

The corrected reading will be 4 4 9 2 8.

DIAL 1
Pointer has passed 4, reading is 4

DIAL 2
Pointer is directly over 5, write down 5 and underline <u>5</u>

DIAL 3
Pointer has passed 9, reading is 9

DIAL 4
Pointer has passed 2, reading is 2.

DIAL 5
Pointer is directly over 8, write down 8 and underline <u>8</u>

10000   1000   100   10   1kWh

Ignore this dial →

As with the digital meter, when you've worked out the reading, subtract the previous reading shown on your bill to find the number of units of electricity used.

NB: If you pay for your electricity through a landlord's meter, bear in mind that your Electricity Board will have fixed a maximum price for the resale of this electricity. Ask your Electricity Board for further details.

REMEMBER: Before you read your dial meter, check the direction of your dials. They may not be exactly like those illustrated in the meter above. Remember every dial on every meter revolves from 0 through 1 and on to 9 before continuing on to 0.

Points to note

a) Always write down the number the pointer has *passed* (this is not necessarily the nearest number to the pointer).
So if the pointer is anywhere between, say, 4 and 5, write down 4.

b) If the pointer is directly over a figure, say 5, write down that figure and underline it. <u>5</u>

c) The sample meter reading shown will be 4 <u>5</u> 9 2 <u>8</u>. This reading now requires

Assignment 26:
Starting work

In this assignment you will be asked to do various tasks in which you build up a picture of your workplace, or work experience placement, and record it in a way that will be helpful to another student or trainee going to work in the same place. You may be working in a large place, such as a hospital, or a small place such as a day centre. Either way, this assignment is about your immediate working environment and people within it, not the larger organisation. In Assignment 28 'The hospital at work' you are asked to find out about how a large institution such as a hospital works.

**TASK 1:
GETTING THE
PICTURE**

1 Give a brief outline of your workplace, covering:
- Name of centre or ward;
- An impression of how big, how old, how well maintained the place is;
- How many clients there are;
- Why clients are there; and
- Treatments or activities offered.

2 Make a scale drawing of your ward or centre. Use graph paper. Show the location of:
- main areas, beds, activity areas;
- staff/office areas;
- storage areas;
- resuscitation equipment;
- fire escapes, alarms and equipment;
- treatment rooms;
- toilets, bathrooms;
- amenities for clients.

**TASK 2:
WHO WORKS
THERE?**

1 Make a list of all the different employees who come to the ward or centre in the course of the day. For each write down what you *think* their responsibilities are.

2 With a partner, draw up a questionnaire which will enable you to find out more precisely what the responsibilities of various members of staff are. Be sure to include questions about training/qualifications; skills; and personal qualities necessary for the job.

3 Think carefully about when to use open and closed questions (*see* 'How to draw up a questionnaire' on p 279). When you have drafted your questions, type them, preferably on a word processor, leaving enough space for you to write the answers.

4 Choose two or three members of staff to interview. Try and ensure they do different jobs. It may be a good idea to interview your mentor or supervisor first, and ask them for comments on your questions, and the way you conduct the interview.

Make any changes necessary before interviewing other members of staff.

TASK 3: **THE CLIENTS**	Find out some basic information about the clients. (*a*) How old are they? Present this in a bar chart. (*b*) What illnesses or conditions do they have? Find out some basic information about the most common illness or condition.
TASK 4: **YOUR JOB**	**1** Give an outline of a typical day and what you do through the day. **2** Describe in greater detail two activities you undertook or incidents you were involved in over the past week. Comment on what you did, how you did it, how you felt; how the client(s) responded to you; and how other staff members reacted.
TASK 5: **RECORDING IT ALL**	Design a booklet you could give to another person from your group going to your workplace, giving them essential information. Include selected information from your work on this assignment so far and practical information: (*a*) how to handle enquiries; (*b*) how to give and take messages; (*c*) who is in charge while you are there; (*d*) what to do if you are sick, absent or late; (*e*) policy on confidentiality; and (*f*) essential health and safety. The booklet should be useful, attractive, handy and easy to read.
TASK 6: **TALKING TO** **THE GROUP**	Give a talk to your group about your workplace or placement. This may be the first time you have formally talked to the whole group about your placement so think carefully about what to include from the following suggestions: • selected information from your work on the assignment so far; • a description of the clients and their needs; • your impressions on the quality of care clients receive; • your first impressions and your feelings now; • what you feel you have learnt from the work placement; and • what you have enjoyed most and least.

Assignment 27:
The client's viewpoint

In this assignment you are asked to look at your workplace from the point of view of the client or consumer of the services provided there. Other terms may be used to describe clients where you work; 'patients', 'residents', 'trainees', 'consumers'.

TASK 1:
WHO ARE
YOUR CLIENTS?

1   Take about five minutes to jot down as much as you can about the clients in your workplace; start with age, why they are there, needs, physical or mental conditions. Particular details of clients may stick in your mind.
2   When you have done this, take two minutes in turn to tell the other members of your group about the clients you care for. While you are listening, make notes on what the other participants say. For each speaker, make notes on factual information about clients and the speaker's opinions and attitudes.

After each person has spoken, a listener tells the speaker what points they noted. The speaker then comments on whether (i) the factual information is correct; and (ii) they think the description of their attitudes to their work and clients is accurate.
3   Looking back at your notes on the talks by the members of the group, what have you learnt about the clients you all care for? Pick out three points you think are important, and explain how you think each point should affect the way clients are cared for.

For the rest of this assignment, you are asked to study and get to know one client in your care. Before you approach the client, show the assignment to your supervisor or mentor, and discuss with them the best way to go about asking the client for their help.

TASK 2:
WHO MAKES
CONTACT?

1   For a day, make a note of everyone your client makes contact with. You will probably end up with a list that includes professional care workers (e.g. nurse, student nurse, OT), other employees (e.g. catering staff), and others including yourself, other clients and visitors. To record your observations, take a whole sheet of paper, write your client's name in the centre, and draw a line out to everyone they made contact with that day.

2 In a different coloured pen, mark the relationships or contacts you think meant most, or brought most satisfaction to your client

3 Compare your chart with those of others in your group. What conclusions can you draw about how much contact and care 'official' and 'unofficial' carers give? Who do you think are the most important people in making the day pleasant for your client?

TASK 3: A DAY IN THE LIFE OF . . . .

Try and arrange to spend as much time as possible one day with the client you are studying. Agree this with your supervisor first. You may be able to keep the client company and do things with them, or arrange to accompany the client to other places they go to in the course of the day, such as physiotherapy, x-ray.

(*a*) Record your client's day as a 'timetable' showing what they are doing, who they are talking to, what is happening. Make a specific point of checking every half hour. Include the times they are 'doing nothing'. Use a 24-hour clock for your record.

(*b*) Comment on the way your client spent the day.

(*c*) Can you suggest any changes that would be

(i) acceptable to the client; and

(ii) possible for the staff to achieve?

TASK 4: GETTING TO KNOW YOUR CLIENT

Your purpose here is to get to know your client as an individual, and to do this by talking to them, aware always that your client may not want to share private information with you. If it is not practicable for you to do this task, do Task 5 below in greater detail.

Before you start

1 (*a*) Consider how to carry out the task; notes to write up later? a tape recording? Ask your client which they prefer.

(*b*) Work out the questions you would like to ask. Some of the points below may give you starting points.

- their past – what life was like when they were younger
- do they come from another country or another part of the country? How do they like it here?
- what they can and cannot do now; how their condition came about;
- how they feel about being cared for here; what they miss, what they like.
- are there any little changes in how things run that would make life better for your client? Can you do something to help?

2 Present your study as a 'Case History'; past, onset of condition; present.

TASK 5: RESEARCHING A CONDITION

Identify an illness, condition or accident that has affected one or more clients in your place of work. Find out more about it and write up your findings under these headings, if possible:

- causes
- symptoms
- incidence (i.e. how common it is)

- treatments
- services that help
- experience or people affected and their families.

You can talk to your tutor and staff at work as a starting point, and follow up with library research.

Assignment 28:
The hospital at work

The purpose of this assignment is to gain an overview of the organisation of a hospital to get a sense of how it works and how individuals and groups of workers fit into the whole. Any job in a hospital will bring you into contact with a lot of different people doing a lot of different jobs. In the course of a career in the caring services you may well find that you do a number of different jobs too.

The hospital group

The hospital unit you work in may be one of a group of hospitals, which between them provide the full range of services for the population of the district. Below is an outline of the way these services might be organised:
1 **Acute Hospital Services Unit**
2 **Mental Health Services Unit**
3 **Community Services Unit.** Included here are
   - Health centres, clinics;
   - Hospital and community health care for the elderly,
   - Services for people with a physical disability, and
   - Services for people with learning difficulties.
This pattern of provision may change from 1991, with the implementation of the government's changes, as Part 1 explained.

TASK 1:
YOUR HOSPITAL
GROUP

(a) Find out which of the above units your work placement is in.
(b) Find out the range of services, and the units they are within, provided by your hospital or hospital group.
(c) Mark these on a map of your area. You may need a copy of a street map or a plan of a single site, or a smaller scale map showing several towns.
(d) Design a 'Handy Card', that can be kept in a wallet, bag or pocket, with the names, addresses, phone numbers and brief summary of services offered of the hospital services in the group.

TASK 2:
THE ACUTE UNIT

1   Below, in Column 1, are some of the services that may be offered in a large acute unit. Copy out the table and in Column 2 record whether your acute unit has these departments and services;

Column 1	Column 2	Column 3	Column 4
Accident and Emergency			
Anaesthesia			
Ante-natal			
Cardiothoracic			
Chiropody			
Dietetics			
Gynaecology			
Haematology			
ITU (Intensive Therapy Unit)			
Neurology			
Occupational therapy			
Oncology			
Orthopaedics			
Pathology			
Patients property			
Patients transport			
Personnel			
Pharmacy			
Physiotherapy			
Psychiatry			
Public Health			
Social Workers			
Speech therapy			
Ultrasound			
Works			
X-ray			
Others			

2   In Column 3 write down briefly what you think each of these departments or services do.

3   Choose 5 (or more) departments or services to find out more about. Note down your findings in Column 4. For example: what is the specialism concerned with? What treatments are offered? Is there a particular type of patient? Make sure that between you the group covers all the departments offered at your hospital, including the ones you added.

4   Share your knowledge within the group to complete your chart.

TASK 3:
HOW TO GET
THERE

1   Write a set of directions from the main entrance to one of the departments you researched in **3** above.

2   Give the directions to a member of the group. Ask them to write down your directions, then check what they have written for accuracy.

3   When they have found the department, ask them what improvements (if any) you need to make to your directions. Make any changes necessary.

Assignment 29:
Working for patients

A great range of jobs have to be done to enable a hospital to carry out its basic function of caring for patients. We all think of doctors and nurses when we think of hospitals, but we are often unaware of the many jobs other people do to enable this patient care to take place.

Think of an operating theatre – the sort of scene you might see on TV in a hospital soap such as *Casualty*. We see skilled doctors and nurses, with sterile green masks and protective clothing, bent over a patient undergoing an operation in an emergency. Take a closer look at the scene – who has done what to enable this to happen?

What happens?	Who was behind the scenes?
Spotlessly clean operating theatre;	*Domestic assistants* working to specific standards of cleanliness
Patient is wheeled in;	*Porters* . . .
Staff don sterile clothing;	*Laundry staff* . . .
Agency nurse given instructions;	*Ward managers* and *personnel* monitor staffing levels and arrange cover;
Surgeon picks up instrument;	*Theatre technician* has checked working order of all equipment;
'5 mls please, nurse'	Essential drugs ordered from pharmacy, checked and delivered
Swabs, equipment handed to surgeon; procedures recorded	Stores ordered, checked, stored distributed by *network of people*
	Medical Records staff file notes

and so on . . . .

TASK 1:
JOBS PEOPLE DO

1 Chart the 'hidden jobs' in your care setting. Copy and complete the sketch below, showing first the **event or process** that you are familiar with (food or linen arriving, minor works being carried out) then extending beyond to show the **tasks** that have been undertaken and **who** has been involved to make this familiar event happen so smoothly.

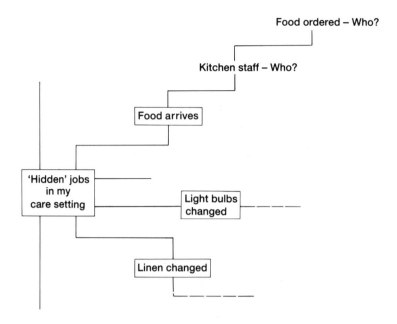

2 List all the jobs you have identified, and compare your list with the ones made by other people in your group. You may need to check some job descriptions. There may be a weekly or monthly 'Vacancy Bulletin' in your hospital, giving you a rough outline of jobs people do.

3 Find out more about four of the jobs you had not thought about before.

**TASK 2:
A DAY IN THE LIFE
OF . . .**

Below is an account of a porter's day at Springfield Hospital, the Mental Health Unit of Wandsworth Health Authority in South London.

A look behind the scenes

A day in the life of a porter

For most of the porters at Springfield shifts either start at 7.00am and end at 3.30pm or start at 11.00am and finish at 8.00pm. Eddy Ryan is one of the few porters who works a regular shift from 7.00am to 4.00pm. His typical day would be as follows:

7.00am

Arrive on duty, pick up the trailer from stores and go to the kitchen to pick up the food trolleys, milk and bread. Deliver these to Gardiner Hill and the Deaf Unit.

8.00am

Return to store to pick up milk and bread and deliver to the wards in the Admissions Block. Transfer black bags to main rubbish collection van and return yellow bags to the incinerator.

9.30am–10.45

On clinic days, escort patients to ECT Department as required. Then pick up post from post room and deliver to District Works, Unit Works, Deaf Unit and Gardiner Hill.

10.45–11.30/11.45

Collect the large trailer from stores and pick up pharmacy bag, CSSD goods, fruit and food from stores. Deliver these to Deaf Unit and Gardiner Hill.

Collect black and yellow rubbish bags from Gardiner Hill and dispose of in mains bins and incinerator.

11.45–12.50

Collect lunch trolley for Jubilee Day Hospital from kitchen and deliver.

Return to kitchen and collect lunch trolleys for delivery to the Deaf Unit and Social Education Centre (SEC).

12.50–1.30

Lunch

1.30–2.30

Collect trolleys from Gardiner Hill, SEC and Deaf UNit (3 trips) and return to kitchen. Dispose of 'swill' en route.

2.30–2.45

Collect post from post room, signing for any recorded deliveries etc.

2.45–4.00pm

Deliver and collect post from Deaf Unit, Gardiner Hill, Juniper OT, Baby Unit, Family Therapy, Occupational Therapy, Occupational Health, Gate Lodge, Cottage Day Hospital and the Regional Education Centre.

Biography

Eddy has been a porter in the NHS since 1963 at a number of hospitals including Charing Cross, Westminster and the Royal Free. He came to Springfield on the closure of St James' in August 1988 and despite initial feelings of trepidation has not regretted the move.

(Reproduced by kind permission of Springfield Hospital, Wandsworth)

1   Choose one of the jobs you identified in Task 1 (**3**), and arrange to interview someone who does the job. Draw up a similar profile of this person's day.

2   When you copy up your interview, rewrite the times using the 24 hour clock. Practise with the porter's day below;

'For most of the porters at Springfield shifts either start at 0700 and end at 1530 or start at 1100 and finish at 2000 . . .'

3   **Discuss** why you think people prefer the 12 hour clock but hospitals use the 24 hour clock to record procedures.

TASK 3:
UNIONS AND
PROFESSIONAL
ORGANISATIONS

In any large organisation with a lot of different people doing different jobs, people will want their voice to be heard and their interests to be taken into account. For this reason, there are a number of trade unions and professional organisations with members in the NHS, and probably in your hospital or care setting.

1   (*a*) What is the full name of each of the following organisations?

(*b*) Which groups of health care workers does each represent?

- COHSE
- BMA

- MDU
- NUPE
- RCN
- RCM
- ASTMS

2   Find out the address and phone number of one of these organisations. Write or phone to ask for an information pack to be sent to you. Make sure that as a group you receive the details of all the organisations.

TASK 4: DO I JOIN?

1   Read carefully the information pack you have received. Your purpose is to tell the group about this organisation. Cover the following points.
- who belongs;
- would you be eligible to join?
- the benefits of joining;
- the costs of joining;
- your views on joining.

2   Listen to the feedback from the other students. Your purpose is to decide which organisations you would be eligible to join. **Discuss** whether you would join.

This discussion could take the form of a **formal debate**. If you decide to do this, arrange it carefully before you start. You need:
- a **motion**, e.g. 'All healthcare workers should belong to a union (or professional organisation)';
- a **Chair** to keep order;
- a **Proposer** and **Seconder** to put the case for joining a particular organisation;
- an **Opposer** and **Seconder** to put the case against joining; and
- an **agreed time limit** for the speakers, to allow time for contributions from the floor.

Procedure
(i)   The Proposer argues the case for the motion.
(ii)   The Opposer puts the case against.
(iii) The Seconder (for) answers the points made by the Opposer.
(iv)   The Seconder (against) criticises the arguments of the Proposer.
(v)   The debate is opened to the 'floor' – the opportunity for everyone else to be invited (by the Chair) to enter into the discussion.
(vi)   When all the points have been aired, one speaker from each side sums up, an opportunity to stress powerful points. A formal debate ends with a vote – but you may decide that this is not the way you want to conclude.

Assignment 30:
Aspects of care

People in need of care have many needs. Some of these will be a direct consequence of their condition and require specific nursing or medical intervention. Others are needs we all have – for company, conversation, activities and interests – but which are harder to fulfil as a result of being in a care setting. This assignment suggests a number of tasks that you may be able to take part in your work setting. It is unlikely that you will be able to do them all, and your tutor will give the guidance on which to do. Several of the tasks follow on well from Assignment 27 'The client's viewpoint'.

TASK 1:
A LITTLE HELP

1 As you get to know your clients, you will become aware of the different needs and preferences of the people you care for. Spend time with one client in particular, perhaps the person you studied in Assignment 27, and work out if there is an activity they would like to do, and could do with your help. It might be
- going for a walk;
- help with appearance; hair care, make up, clothes;
- changing around the client's immediate surroundings (e.g. moving the locker for easier access, arranging photos);
- a particular activity, for example, help with a skill such as knitting, writing a letter;
- adapting something to make it easier for the client to use, e.g. velcro for buttons?

2 Afterwards, write up your activity in report from, showing
(*a*) the problem you identified;
(*b*) what you did to help the client; and
(*c*) the outcome; how successful you think you were in your efforts.

TASK 2:
SELF ASSESSMENT

In most caring courses and training schemes you will be assessed on the skills you display in carrying out tasks in the workplace. Your tutors will discuss with you the particular skills they are looking for in your course of study. Fortunately, all the checklists of skills identified by the different assessment programmes have many features in common and will increasingly correspond to the competences of the new National Vocational Qualifications (NVQ) competences.

In all courses you will have to demonstrate two groups of competences. The first is of **specific tasks** you need to be able to carry out in your work setting. The second concerns your **relationships** with clients; how you support them with sympathy and understanding. These competences are essential to every care worker in every setting. Although the wording of the different assessment programmes may vary, you will need to be able to demonstrate these skills.

Below are some self assessment questions to ask yourself about the activity you carried out in Task 1. They are not taken from any assessment checklist, but are intended to encourage you to think critically about what you did and how you did it.

Self assessment questions	Describe what you did
1 Was my choice of activity a good one? Did the client want or need any help in this activity?	
2 Did I prepare adequately? Through discussion? Did I have the things I needed to hand?	
3 Did I do things in the right order for the client? Did I do things correctly? (eg lifting, supporting)	
4 Was I careful to observe safety and hygiene procedures?	
5 Did I communicate effectively with the client throughout, verbally and non-verbally: How? Did I make it easy for the client to communicate with me?	
6 Was I patient? Was I kind? Reassuring? Not patronising?	
7 Throughout, was I helping the client to do what he or she wanted, or imposing my way of doing things?	

Discuss your answers with your tutor, mentor or other group members.

TASK 3: QUESTIONS OF LIFESTYLE

This task could also follow on from Assignment 27, 'The client's viewpoint'.

Various factors may have contributed to a client's present condition. These include

- **occupation**. Some jobs bring specific health risks.
- **lifestyle choices**. Smoking and drinking, general fitness, diet and stress may have played a part in your client's health.
- **social and economic circumstances**, such as housing, income, employment and unemployment may also have a bearing on your client's present condition.

Find out more about **one** aspect of your client's history and its effect on their health. Many people find these sensitive and private issues, so be aware of being 'nosy'. You may, of course, learn something very positive. Many elderly people brought up their families before junk food was introduced and can tell us a lot about good food.

You may learn a lot from your client. Alternatively, you may be able to use the library, or health promotion materials to find out about effects of occupation and lifestyle.

(*a*) Write up your findings, taking about one side of file paper.

(*b*) Pick out the essential message you have learnt from your research. Design a simple handout on this topic, with a message you think others could learn from.

TASK 4: OCCUPATIONAL THERAPY

You can do this task if you have the opportunity to go with a client to Occupational Therapy. Your task is to report on the session. Set out your report as follows;

1   The client: a brief outline of the client's difficulties and the reason for OT. Find out the thinking behind the activity

2   The activity: give an account of the activity the client takes part in. Use diagrams of equipment or processes where this helps.

3   Evaluate the activity. In what ways has the activity helped the client? This is your own view, but it would help if you can discuss the session with the occupational therapists responsible.

TASK 5: GETTING IN TOUCH

'Reality orientation' is a strategy to help confused, often elderly, clients. It involves drawing to the client's attention a picture or object that engages their attention, to prompt recognition. This recognition can then become the basis for reminiscences. The client can then be encouraged to talk and think about familiar things from the past, and to distinguish between the past and the present.

If you choose this task, it would be helpful if you could attend at least two 'reality orientation' sessions, the first as an observer, the second to take a more active part.

1   After the first session, **write the introduction** to your study.

(*a*) What is 'reality orientation'?

(*b*) When is it used in your care setting?

(*c*) Which clients is it designed to help?

(*d*) How does it work?

2   Plan your contribution to a reality orientation session. Discuss your plans with your mentor, and include their suggestions. Decide what you are going to bring – photographs? Newspaper headlines? Objects, such as a teapot or cup? Music or song?

3   Write up your plans using the headings 'Aim'; 'Plan'; 'Action'; and 'Evaluation'. Turn your page sideways and draw up columns.

Under **AIM** list what you hope to achieve; under **PLAN** list how you plan to carry out your idea; under **ACTION** list what you did in the session; and under **EVALUATION** list how successful you think your contribution was, and include the feedback and comment from the participants and staff.

TASK 6: GETTING READY

You may be asked to help to prepare a trolley for a particular care procedure in the clinical area. This task follows from this activity. Write a short report on what you did, following the outline below.

1   Introduction: who the client is; what condition they have; the nature of the procedure to be carried out; why it has to be done.

2   Preparation: outline the preparations in the care environment before the procedure can be carried out. List these in order.

3   Draw a diagram of the trolley you have prepared or helped to prepare, showing all the items on it. This should occupy a space the size of a postcard in the centre of your page. Draw a line from each item in your diagram to the space around the page, and explain briefly what the item is, and how it works or is used.

4   Afterwards: list the tasks that had to be carried out to restore the clinical environment after the procedure was completed.

Assignment 31:
Coming into hospital

For Task 1 of this assignment you will need to draw on the expertise of an experienced nurse. The assignment could be used as a basis for discussion with an outside speaker.

Background information

You are working as a Healthcare Assistant in a General Medical ward of a general hospital. An old lady is brought up to your ward, unconscious, and looking pale, and frail. You are not involved in admitting her but you learn what has happened.

The ambulance had been called by someone visiting her at about 10 am who had found her unconscious at the bottom of the stairs in her nightdress. It seems that she had been there for some time as she was very cold. The medical and nursing staff establish that she has had a fairly minor stroke, but it caused her to fall downstairs. She is suffering from extensive bruising – although no broken bones – shock, cold and the after-effects of the stroke.

When you come to work the following day, she is conscious, but appears to be asleep much of the time. As the morning goes by she looks around a little. She cannot speak, although she seems able to hear when staff talk to her. A **nursing care plan** has been drawn up for her, and you will be asked to carry out certain tasks in that care plan under the direction of a nurse.

The Activities of Daily Living is a structure for thinking about the needs of an ill person. You will see that the 14 headings of the 'Activities of Daily Living' (or 'ADL') form on p 45 lists the essential functions a person has to carry out to sustain a healthy physical and psychological life. The assessment process encourages carers to see a person's difficulties with a physical or a psychological problem as a specific problem that can be solved or relieved by specific medical, nursing or care procedures. So the carer approaches a client to find out:

● Which of these essential ADL functions does this person need help with?

● How, as carers, can we help to restore a person with an illness or disability to a point where they can carry out these tasks for themselves?

Some of the answers to these questions will require medical intervention; others will require skilled nursing; others thoughtful care.

TASK 1: PLANNING CARE

This task can be carried out as a group activity in discussion with an experienced nurse, or individually, referring to a registered practitioner.

Copy the blank assessment form on p 46 and complete it for this patient. Refer to the full ADL assessment list on p 45 when you are discussing whether a particular area is likely to be a problem for this patient.

1 Identify the **problems** this patient will have under each of the ADL headings and enter these in Column 1. You may decide that some do not apply – but think carefully before entering this.

2 Head Column 2 **'Nursing Aims'.** Identify the nursing aims for each area and enter these here.

3 Head Column 3 **'Healthcare Assistant's tasks'.** Enter here the tasks an HCA might be asked to carry out under the direction of a registered practitioner in each ADL area.

TASK 2: A FAMILIAR FACE

This patient you have been discussing is Mrs Nellie Taylor from Case Study 6. Mrs O'Brien found Mrs Taylor and called the ambulance.

1 Look back at the Healthcare Assistant's tasks in the ADL form mentioned above. Now you know a little more about this lady, can you add any suggestions on how to approach the tasks you have listed?

2 Discuss what difference you think it makes to the care a client receives when the carer knows the person. What difference does it make to a carer?

TASK 3: WHAT DO YOU SEE, NURSES?

Read this poem and then answer the following questions.

1 What is your reaction to the poem? Pick out one or two bits that you find particularly moving. Explain why.

2 Pick out the specific things you can see are wrong with the care Kate received. Double check this with the ADL list. Which of these essential needs have been not been addressed by Kate's carers? Relate your comments to the poem whenever possible.

3 How do you think Kate's care could have been improved? Make a list of your ideas.

What do you see?

What do you see, nurses,
What do you see?
Are you thinking,
When you are looking at me;
A crabbit old woman,
Not very wise,
Uncertain of habit,
With far away eyes,
Who dribbles her food
And makes no reply
When you say in a loud voice
'I do wish you'd try',
Who seems not to notice
The things that you do,
And forever is losing
A stocking or shoe,
Who, unresisting or not,
Lets you do as you will,
With bathing and feeding,
The long day to fill.
Is that what you're thinking,
Is that what you see?

Then open your eyes, nurse.
You're not looking at me.
As I'll tell you who I am,
As I sit here so still,
As I rise at your bidding,
As I eat at your will.

I'm a small child of ten
With a mother and father,
Brothers and sisters,
Who love one another.

A young girl of sixteen,
With wings on her feet,
Dreaming that soon now
A lover she'll meet;

A bride soon at twenty;
My heart gives a leap,
Remembering the vows
That I promised to keep;

At twenty-five now
I have young of my own,
Who need me to build
A secure, happy home.

A young woman of thirty,
My young now grow fast,
Bound to each other
With ties that should last;

At forty, my young ones,
Now grown, will soon be gone,
But my man stays beside me,
To see I don't mourn.

At fifty once more,
Babies play round my knee.
Again we know children,
My loved one and me.

Dark days are upon me,
My husband is dead,
I look at the future,
I shudder with dread,
For my young are all busy,
Rearing young of their own,
And I think of the years
And the love I have known.

I'm an old woman now,
And nature is cruel.
'Tis her jest to make old age
To look like a fool.
The body is crumbled,
Grace and vigour depart.
There is now a stone
Where I once had a heart.

But inside this old carcass,
A young girl still dwells,
And now and again
My battered heart swells.
I remember the joys,
I remember the pain,
And I'm loving and living
Life over again.

I think of the years,
All too few
Gone too fast,
And accept the stark fact
That nothing can last.

So open your eyes, nurses,
Open and see,
Not a crabbit old woman;
Look closer . . . see ME.

*Kate, the writer of this poem, was unable
to speak, but was occasionally seen to write.
After her death, her locker at Napsbury
Hospital, near St Albans, Herts, was emptied
and this poem was found.*

(Published in The Health Service Journal,
18/25 December 1986).

Communicating

Many of the points you made in Task 3 will be about problems with **communication**. Your concern now is to make sure that Mrs Taylor is treated with sensitivity and dignity. This task is about asking questions so that someone without speech can exercise as much choice and control as possible.

Open and closed questions

You have been asked to find out what Mrs Taylor would like for lunch. Look at the two styles of questions below and decide which is the most effective in finding out what Mrs Taylor would like for lunch.

A 'Would you like roast potatoes and beef, or shepherds pie and carrots, Mrs Taylor?'

B 'Would you like roast potatoes and beef, Mrs Taylor?'
'No? Would you like shepherds pie?'
'Yes? and carrots?'
'No? I'll ask for shepherds pie without carrots. Is that right, Mrs Taylor?'

Question A requires several words in an answer: it is an **open question**. This sort of question can draw out people's thoughts, opinions and reactions, and does not restrict their answers. 'What would you like for lunch?' is a completely open question, to which everyone could give a different answer, depending on their preferences. You are not likely to ask that in hospital, when the menu offers a limited choice. Mrs Taylor, however, cannot respond to the restricted choice offered in Question A because she cannot speak.

The questions in B can be answered with a 'Yes' or 'No' or by the slightest gesture – a nod or shake of the head. They are **closed questions**. Closed questions enable someone without speech to communicate and exercise choice.

**TASK 4:
WHAT WOULD YOU
LIKE?**

You have been asked to find out what Mrs. Taylor would like for lunch and supper tomorrow. Write out the questions you might ask her to find out exactly what she would like from one of the menus on pp 196–7.

When you have designed your questions, try them out on a partner to make sure that they can be answered by someone with no speech. Make any changes necessary.

**TASK 5:
REMEMBER**

In a busy care setting, especially when the clients are highly dependent, it is easy to see how the thoughtless practices that distressed Kate can happen. But it is important as carers to guard against the attitudes and routines that give rise to this situation.

Design a poster or handy card you think would be effective in reminding staff to be sensitive to the needs of each individual client. In designing it you need to decide:

- the **message** you want to convey;
- **who** you want your message to reach; and
- how to **circulate** or where to **display** your message.

Assignment 32:
Teamwork

Most of our time is spent with groups of other people – helping one another, arguing, making decisions, compromising, talking, having fun. We need to get on with people both at home and at work.

TASK 1:
YOU IN A GROUP

The diagram below shows some of the different groups a person might spend time with. Draw a similar one for yourself.

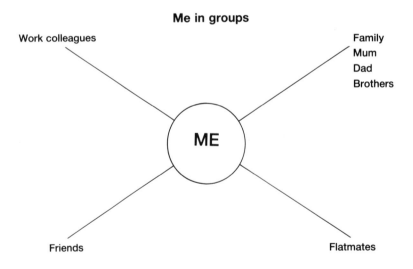

Take a few minutes to answer these questions on your own:
(a) Which group is most important to you?
(b) Which groups are you most happy to be a member of?
(c) Which groups are you least happy to be a member of?
(d) What factors might cause your membership of a group to change?
(e) What is the best thing about your group of friends?

(*f*) What is the best thing about the group you work with?
(*g*) Do you take a leading role in any of these groups?
(*h*) How do you think other group members see you in the group?
(*i*) Are you satisfied with the way you contribute to and take part in your groups? Which ones?

TASK 2: WORKING AS PART OF A TEAM

1 Here are some comments made by people discussing working as part of a team.

- I can't think of anything to say
- She's too bossy
- No one asks my opinion
- I usually get my ideas through
- I'm not sure what I'm supposed to do
- If I say what I really think it'll get back to my boss
- My job is so boring
- I'm a natural talker
- Everyone else knows much more than me
- No one listens to what I say
- We never get anywhere

Can you add any others?

2 In small groups decide the reasons for each of the comments. Note which ones you feel apply to you.

3 On your own, write a paragraph on 'What happens when I work in a team.'

TASK 3: THE COMMUNICATION SKILLS CHECKLIST

In this task you are asked to think about the skills you need for successful group work.

1 (*a*) Here is a self-analysis checklist which you should copy out. Answer 'yes' or 'no' in Column 1 to show how you react in groups. You will fill in Columns 2 and 3 later.

Self-analysis checklist	1	2	3
	Yes/No		
Do I speak too much sometimes?			
Do I speak too little sometimes?			
Do I listen to others?			
Can they tell I am listening?			
Do I help other members of the group?			
Do people listen to what I say?			
Do I make people comfortable?			
Do I work out what I'm doing?			
Do I like being the leader of the group?			
Do I stay calm?			
Do I always speak clearly?			

(*b*) Discuss which you think are the most important skills in group work.

2 Now write a few words on how you could improve your group skills: 'Next time I work as part of a group I will try to . . .'

TASK 4:
FIGHT IT OUT!
A BALLOON DEBATE

The story is that six people are in a hot air balloon. They are:
- a hospital porter;
- a patient;
- a visiting relative
- a staff nurse;
- a care assistant; and
- a consultant.

Six people in the group need to volunteer to be the 'balloonists'.

The balloon is in trouble and is rapidly falling into the deep sea and, if anybody is to survive, four people must be thrown out immediately. Who has to go? The group should decide.

Round 1: Each character has two to three minutes to convince the spectactors why they are important and should survive. After hearing these speeches the spectators must agree on which four will be thrown out and which two remain.

Round 2: The balloon continues to dive. It can only support one person. The final two speak again and answer any questions the spectators ask of them. The spectators then decide on the final survivor.

Review: Teamwork or competition?

The balloonists: Did you 'do well'? or 'do badly'? How do you feel about winning and losing? What effect does this sort of competition have on your relationships with your companions? What techniques of argument did you use to try and stay airborne? How does it compare with teamwork?

The spectators: Were you aware of competitive emotions in the balloonists? How did you make your decisions on who to throw out? Which skills in the checklist (*see* p 245) did you use? Mark them in Column 2.

TASK 5:
TEAMWORK –
MARKETING YOUR
COURSE

You have been asked how best to publicise your course, in order to attract enough new students next year to set up another, parallel group. This is an exercise in teamwork; so use all your group skills to produce the best possible marketing plan.

Work in groups of six to eight people. A further three or four people to each group will act as observers. The observers need to have the self-analysis checklists of the people in their group, two each. They will fill in Column 3 of the checklist on p 245 for the participants as they watch the discussion. Agree on a time limit.

1   **A marketing plan.** Consider:
- your target groups;
- your methods; and
- your campaign – various tactics? a special event?

2   **How well did you work?**

(*a*) Present your marketing plan to the group tutor.

(*b*) Observers should then feed back their observations on how each group worked and made decisions, commenting on the checklist skills they saw – or did not see – in action.

3   Observers should return the checklists to the participants and explain their reasons for the assessment they made in Column 3.

Assignment 33:

Facts and figures – a case study of a region

South West Thames region produces an attractive leaflet giving essential facts and figures about the services in the region illustrating the following data.

TASK 1:
SPENDING ON
SERVICES

SPENDING ON SERVICES

Services	(£m) **1988/89**
General and acute	206.6
Children	12.0
Maternity	40.8
Geriatrics	45.7
Mental illness	74.0
Mental handicap	54.0
Administration	73.2
Blood Transfusion Service	3.7
Ambulance services	51.7
Regional specialities	40.3
Community and prevention	73.5
Estates	44.6
Training	22.7
Energy	12.7
Cleaning, catering, laundry, portering and others	73.7
Total	829.2

Included in several of the above are: Medical and surgical supplies
(£22.6m) and Drugs (£20.0m)

Present this data in the form of an easy to read bar chart.

TASK 2:
NUMBER OF
NHS STAFF

Draw a pie chart to present the following data:

Staff group	Numbers
Nurses and midwives	22 800
Professional, Scientific and Technical	4 300
Administrative and Clerical	6 300
Ancillary	5 400
Ambulance	3 500
Medical and Dental	2 500
Other	1 300
Total	46 100

(numbers given in whole time equivalents)

TASK 3:
STATE OF THE
REGION'S HEALTH

Incidence of the most common causes of death

	Deaths per year		
	Males	**Females**	**Total**
Cancer	4 175	4 204	8 379
Heart disease	5 015	5 078	10 093
Respiratory	1 725	1 777	3 502
Cardiovascular (strokes)	1 436	2 775	4 211
Other	3 225	4 133	7 358
Total	15 576	17 967	33 553

Decide what you want to present here – the overall numbers, or incidence of these diseases in men and women. Then decide how best to present the data.

TASK 4:
HOSPITAL ACTIVITY

HOSPITAL ACTIVITY: Bed numbers

Regional summary 1988/89

	Day cases	**In-patients**	**Out-patients**	**Available beds**
General and acute	48 981	246 861	1 571 325	5 795
Children	155	57 703	44 024	620
Maternity	1 158	48 272	151 373	770
Geriatrics	107	21 996	18 760	2 705
Mental illness	88	13 828	109 224	4 840
Mental handicap	0	4 870	4 968	4 070
Total	50 489	393 530	1 899 674	18 800

(a) How many maternity in-patients were there? How long on average did each patient stay?

(b) (i) How many 'General and Acute' patients were treated per bed that year?

(ii) How long was the average stay in hospital of 'general and acute' patients?

(c) What do you observe about the number of mental handicap in-patients to beds? Why do you think this is?

(d) Look back to the categories of services outlined in Assignment 28. How many beds in the South West Thames Region Health Authority are for:

(i) Acute Hospital Services;

(ii) Mental Health Services; and

(iii) Community Services?

(e) What use are each of these service areas able to make of:

(i) outpatient appointments and clinics; and

(ii) day care treatment?

Why do you think this is?

TASK 5: A PROFILE IN YOUR REGION

1 **Discussion point:** where do you go to find this sort of information about your region (or district)?

2 Find out the facts and figures about your region using the headings in Tasks 1–4. Present a 'Facts and Figures' brochure, based on the data.

Assignment 34:
Job search 1:
Where next?

You will have seen a great range of jobs in caring in this book; it can be hard to decide what to do next after training. This assignment asks you to survey job options, and to see where you might fit in after considering your own strengths, weaknesses and history.

TASK 1:
WHAT'S ON OFFER?

1 With a partner scan this book and make a note of all the different jobs in caring mentioned. Write 'Job Search' in the middle of your page and add each job on a branch out. Similar jobs can go on the same branch. Assignments 27, 29 and the Service Checklist on pp 33–7 are useful starting points.

2 Choose one job that interests you and arrange to see someone who does this job. Your tutor and other group members may have useful contacts. The purpose of your meeting is to find out more about their job.

(a) *Before your meeting.* Write down eight to ten questions you would like to ask; include training, pay and conditions, duties, advantages and disadvantages of the job.

(b) *After your meeting.*

(i) write a letter of thanks to the person you interviewed;

(ii) present a profile of this person's job to your group. End with your own impressions, and whether you still want to work in this area.

TASK 2:
WHAT SORT OF
PERSON ARE YOU?

Whether you enjoy a job or not will depend largely on the kind of person you are. In this task you are asked to make a self-assessment of your personal characteristics as a starting point for decision making.

1 Work with a partner.

(a) On your own, pick out ten words from the list below you think best describe you. Then pick out the ten words you think best describe your partner.

(b) Compare lists. Discuss the reasons for any differences.

Words to describe you

Adaptable	Honest
Aggressive	Idealistic
Arrogant	Impatient
Articulate	Independent
Assertive	Inquisitive
Authoritative	Meticulous
Bland	Outgoing
Bossy	Panicky
Brave	Patient
Caring	Passive
Careless	Outgoing
Cheerful	Quickthinking
Communicative	Reliable
Easygoing	Resourceful
Energetic	Self-assured
Flexible	Shy
Friendly	Studious
Funny	Tactful
Happy	Understanding
Hardworking	

---

2   Strengths and weaknesses

Below is a list of skills and abilities. Make two lists – list 1 headed; 'Things I am good at'; and list 2 headed, 'Things I am not so good at'.

Words to describe strengths and weaknesses

Advising others	Managing my time
Asking questions	Motivating others
Asserting myself	Organising myself
Budgeting	Organising others
Coping	Persuading
Delegating	Planning ahead
Explaining	Remembering details
Helping	Responding to others
Initiating	Sympathising
Learning new things	Taking responsibility
Learning from mistakes	Talking
Listening	Teaching
Making new contacts	Timekeeping
Making decisions	Understanding
Managing other people	Writing

When you have written your list, you can keep it private. If you decide to show it to your partner, ask for their comments on your assessment of your strengths and weaknesses. Their views will be helpful in seeing how others see you.

TASK 3: YOUR CURRICULUM VITAE

A curriculum vitae, or CV, is your life history in a nutshell. Whereas an application form asks you to consider your experience in the light of the demands of a particular job, in a CV you set out basic factual information.

Make sure you prepare a CV now and update it in the future to show recent courses, qualifications and experiences. It is an invaluable record in filling in application forms.

1 Make a rough draft of your CV. Head it with your name, and use these headings:

Curriculum Vitae

First name and family name

Personal details
Address

Tel
Date of birth

Education and qualifications

Dates	Schools attended	Qualifications
	Colleges attended	

Employment history (in order)
If you have not worked before include Saturday jobs, work experience. If you have no work experience, leave this section out.

Dates	Employer	Post and brief description of work

Other experience
Include here voluntary work, involvement in local organisations or groups, sport, genuine interests.

Referees
Give the names, positions and addresses of two people who would be willing to act as referee for you. Ask first.

---

2   Discuss your rough draft with your tutor. When you have a final version, type it neatly, preferably on a word processor so you can make changes. It is essential to get it well laid out, without any mistakes. Aim for no more than **one side** of A4, unless you really can justify the extra space.

Assignment 35:
Job search 2:
Applying for a job

TASK 1:
WHERE TO LOOK?

Where will you find advertisements for the sorts of jobs you want to apply for? There are

general sources; job centres, newspapers, local, national, ethnic minority; employment agencies;

specialist sources: magazines (e.g. *Nursing Times, Community Care*), specialist newspapers (e.g. *Guardian Society* on Wednesdays), friends and contacts.

In pairs, check out each of the sources above, and find one advertisement for a job you could apply for from each. Take down details, cut them out, or photocopy them and paste them onto file paper, noting the source and date underneath.

TASK 2:
READING THE ADS

Shown on pp 256–7 are a number of adverts for jobs in caring. Read them and answer these questions:

1 (*a*) Which jobs are unpaid? Under what circumstances would you consider doing one of these?

(*b*) Which jobs provide training?

(*c*) Which jobs require prior experience?

(*d*) Which employers state that they are committed to equal opportunities? What do you think this means?

(*e*) Which jobs could you apply for with your present qualifications and experience?

(*f*) Some adverts do not give rates of pay. Why do you think this is?

2 **Pay.** Details of pay can be given as an hourly, weekly, monthly or annual rate. This makes comparison difficult.

Draw up a chart with these headings and work out the rate of pay for the jobs that give pay rates. Make sure you know how to do the calculation – a month is not four weeks!

TASK 3:
PLEASE SEND ME
FURTHER DETAILS . . .

Look back at the advert you collected in Task 1. Ask for further details for **three** of these. If possible, telephone for two adverts and write for one. This is your first contact with a possible employer, so think carefully about the impression you create.

COMMUNITY CARE ASSISTANTS

This is an ideal opportunity for practical and resourceful people with a genuine interest in caring for others to start work within the caring profession.

You will help clients in their own homes with a range of everyday personal tasks. The ability to work alone is essential and a sense of humour helps. With friendly and supportive supervisors and regular training, you will find the work extremely worthwhile.

We have five vacancies, four full-time and one part-time and need people to cover various hours of work including some weekends. you will receive enhanced pay for weekend and evening work plus a travel pass allowance.

c.£160 per week

We are an equal opportunity employer.

COLLEGE OF NURSING & MIDWIFERY

STUDENT NURSE TRAINING
PROJECT 2000

Following the successful implementation of Project 2000 within this College we are now interviewing for the few remaining places (Registered Mental Nurse and Registered Nurse Mentally Handicapped) for 1991.

These courses are diploma level (with full student status and grant), with opportunity on completion to undertake a part-time degree course.

Successful candidates will be based at either Redditch, Kidderminster, Hereford or Worcester (accommodation provided).

If you are 17½ - 50, in a rut and want a challenging and satisfying career write now for further details, enclosing list of all educational qualifications (level, subject and grade) to:

Recruitment & Personnel Officer

THE GUINNESS TRUST

requires

Staff for its elderly people's home in St.John's Wood/Primrose Hill. We are looking for mature caring individuals with a commitment to the well being of elderly people. Previous experience in this field would be an advantage.

Hours: 37½ per week on a rota basis including some weekends, but we would be interested in hearing from people who want to work part time i.e mornings only, evenings only or on a job share basis.

Salary: £4.12 per hour.

As part of the Trust's Equal Opportunities Policy, we welcome applications, regardless of race, colour, disability, marital status or sex.

 Interested in meeting new people?
ONE-TO-ONE ONE TO ONE
is looking for
VOLUNTEERS

to enable people with learning difficulties (mental handicap) to improve their quality of life through increased opportunities for friendships. choice and independence.

Training and support given. If you can make a regular commitment over several months and would like further information then contact your local co-ordinator.

NOTE TO TUTOR: STUDENTS SHOULD NOT CONTACT THE ORGANISATIONS SHOWN IN THE JOB ADVERTS, WHICH HAVE BEEN SHOWN FOR DEMONSTRATION PURPOSES ONLY.

Remember: Your purpose in contacting the employer is to ask for further details and application forms. The application itself comes later. Keep your letter or telephone call short, polite and correct.

- **Do** read the advert carefully before you contact the employer;
- **Do not** address the contact person by their first name – use Mr, Mrs or Ms;
- **Do** make sure you know the name of the organisation, and the name or position of the person you are contacting.

When you phone
- **Do** know exactly what you are going to say when your call is answered;
- **Do** speak clearly, and be prepared to spell your name and address.

When you write
- **Do** write in dark blue or black ink;
- **Do** make sure your letter is neat. If you make a mistake, start again;
- **Do not** write on work paper, lined paper, fancy or scented paper.

(For instructions on letter layout, *see* 'How to set out letters' on p 276.)

TASK 4: READING THE DETAILS

The envelopes that come through your letter box will contain
- an **application form**;
- a **job description**, short or long, detailing the tasks a job entails;
- maybe a **person specification** detailing the skills, abilities and experiences that are 'essential' or 'desirable' in the person wishing to apply for the post.

You must read these details carefully to decide
- whether you want the job;
- whether you stand a chance of getting the job;
- what to include in your application

You have received this job description from Deseworth Health Authority.

1 Read the job description opposite and then with a partner answer these questions:
   (*a*) What is the title of this job?
   (*b*) Who will be your immediate boss?
   (*c*) What is meant by these phrases
        (i) 'supporting (residents) in realising their full potential' (Aims 1); and
        (ii) 'maintaining individuality and independence' (Aims 2)?
   (*d*) In what ways could you be an 'efficient and effective link' between the housing association and the Community Services Unit?
2 Which of the following duties does this job entail?
   - preparing food
   - administration
   - record keeping
   - shopping
   - providing information
   - implementing policies

DESEWORTH HEALTH AUTHORITY

COMMUNITY SERVICES UNIT

JOB DESCRIPTION

Grade: 'B'
Job Title: Care Assistant
Base: 6 Firbank Road
Reports to: House Manager

AIMS OF THE POST

1. To enable a group of residents to live in a domestic setting whilst supporting them in realising their full potential.

2. To promote a high standard of care, support and supervision whilst maintaining individuality and independence.

3. To operate as an efficient and effective link in the partnership between the Association and the Unit.

MAIN DUTIES

1. To assist in the administrative duties of the house as required.

2. To assist with the safe custody and maintenance of resident's records.

3. Ensure confidentiality is maintained.

4. Report on the daily affairs of the house and seek help and support when necessary.

5. Participate in the implementation of agreed procedures and policies.

6. Actively participate in multi-disciplinary meetings and reviews.

7. Liaise with all staff and support services, both within the house and in the community.

8. Assist in arranging for residents to attend doctors, dentists, chiropodists and opticians, escorting them when necessary.

9. Where necessary, assist residents with personal hygiene and appearance.

10. Work with the residents, providing support, teaching and supervision with their domestic duties, such as cleaning, laundry, cooking, shopping and budgeting when appropriate.

11. Work in accordance with the Health and Safety at Work Act and agreed policies, and ensure that hazards and the need to repair equipment are identified and reported promptly.

12. Be familiar with and observe the fire procedure.

13. Participate in the development of residents' programmes and report progress at team meetings.

JOBDES.J
12.12.9

- designing policies
- budgeting
- teaching
- maintaining standards of cleanliness
- interviewing
- contributing to meetings
- liaising with other staff
- making doctor's appointments
- assisting with personal hygiene
- escorting residents on outings
- planning outings
- ensuring confidentiality
- reporting residents' progress
- taking responsibility for new staff
- designing development programmes for residents

3   Your personal qualities. The job you are applying for may not have a person specification – the Firbank Road one, for example, did not. Nevertheless, you need to think as much about your personal qualities and experiences, as you do about the specific tasks.

(*a*) There are hints in the job description above about the personal qualities and attitudes the interviewers will be looking for. As a group pick out at least one personal quality for each point in the job description. List them on the board.

(*b*) Copy down the list of personal qualities. Work with a partner.

    (i) On your own, tick the personal qualities you think you could offer. Then tick the ones you think your partner can offer.

    (ii) Compare lists. As in Job search 1, discuss the reasons for any differences.

TASK 5:
COMPLETING THE
APPLICATION FORM

1   Personal details. This is where your CV comes in useful; all your details are ready for entering on the application form such as the example shown opposite. Read the following tips carefully before completing your application form.

- **Photocopy** the form, and fill in your dummy in pencil first;
- **Read** the whole form carefully before you start to fill it in;
- **Use block letters** where it says to;
- **Use black ink** and write on a clean, flat surface;
- **Avoid deletion** or smudges; keep this for your dummy;
- **Answer all questions** Enter N/A to any questions which do not apply to you;
- **Write clearly** and neatly;
- **Check** what you have written before sending it off.
- **Choose your referees** carefully and ask permission to use their names. Explain them what the job entails and why you are applying for it.

2   The supporting statement. Nobody finds writing this easy – it is by far the hardest part of any application form, but it is perhaps the most important. It is the only chance you have to say what *you* want to say about why you want the job, and your suitability for it.

ref.				
Closing date (if any)	DAY	MONTH	YEAR	

Application For

Job	Department

Personal Details

First names	Surname
Address	Date of birth — DAY MONTH YEAR
	TICK BOX Male ☐ Female ☐
	Telephone Work: Home:

Education

Schools/colleges etc since age 13	Dates	Qualifications		
	from to	subjects	grade	dates

Please give details of any courses presently being undertaken

Membership of professional organisations (give status and dates)

Other Training

Any other relevant training, skills or course (give dates)

Employment History

Employer's name and address	Job title	salary	Dates	
			from	to
Current job first				

Please give a simple diagram to show your position in the organisation

Experience

Please summarise the main duties and responsibilities in your current or most recent job.

Please give an outline of your experience from other jobs and describe your main achievements or say why you might be suitable for this job.

Continue on a separate sheet if necessary

References

Please give two referees, one whom should be your present or most recent employer. Please do not give friends or relatives

name	name
job title	job title
address	address
relationship	relationship
May we contact them at this stage?	May we contact them at this stage?

Other Questions

Period of notice required by present employer	Please give any dates over coming weeks when you will be unavailable for interviews
Do you have a current driving licence?	Tick box NO ☐ YES ☐ → Do you have use of a car during working hours?
Are you a registered disabled person?	Tick box NO ☐ YES ☐ → If so, please give registration number
Are you related to any senior officer or elected member of this council?	Tick box NO ☐ YES ☐ → If so, please state name and relationship
Do you need a permit to work in the UK?	Tick box NO ☐ YES ☐ → If so, please give details
Do you receive a local government pension?	

Outside Interests

Please give brief details of spare time interests and activities

- If any particulars given by you in this application are found to be false, or if you wilfully omit or suppress any material facts you will, if appointed, be liable to dismissal. Any canvassing, direct or indirect, for appointments or contracts with the council is strictly prohibited and will disqualify candidates
- Please note that we do not normally acknowledge receipt of applications - sorry! Also, it is not always possible for us to reply to every application. Shortlisted candiates are normally called for interview within 3 /4 weeks. If you do not hear by then, please assume that you have been unsuccessful.

I declare that to the best of my knowledge and belief the information given is correct.
Signed: Date:

Where did you see this vacancy advertised?

In your supporting statement you must show that

(a) *You understand the aims of the post.* Start your statement with one or two sentences about why you are applying for this post, and what attract you about it.

(b) *You can carry out the duties.* Show how your experience suits you for the job. Do not repeat your life history – this is on the form – but link your experience to the duties of the job.

(c) *You have the necessary personal qualities.* Pick out something from your experience that helps to show your suitability; or show how the jobs links with an interest; or how it develops your career plans.

Draft your supporting statement following the structure above. Discuss it with your tutor. When you are satisfied with it, copy it carefully onto your application form.

Do make sure you keep a copy of your form.

TASK 6: THE INTERVIEW

Interviews are sometimes described as a two-way conversation in which you and the employer find out whether you are suited. This is, of course, true, but it does not usually feel like that. You want to be offered the job and to present yourself as well as you possibly can. So it is important to think it through . . .

1 **Before the interview**
   - read through the original advert and job description
   - check the time and location of the interview
   - plan your journey
   - find out as much as you can about the institution
   - think about the questions you will ask in the interview
   - think about the questions you may be asked and plan your answers
   - decide what you are going to wear.

2 **During the interview**
   - be clear about the impression you want to create
   - answer questions clearly and cheerfully
   - if you don't understand a question ask for it to be repeated.
   - do not be distracted by your interviewer's face or mannerisms
   - control your own movements and do not fiddle with clothing or jewellery
   - think positive and not only want the job but intend to get it.

3 **Some questions**

Here are some of the questions that are most commonly asked in one form or another. How would **you** answer them? The interview is for the post as Care Assistant at Firbank Road. Use the notes to help you.

Questions	**Notes**
1 What made you decide to apply for this job?	Have two or three reasons for applying. Tie in your answer with your training and experience.
2 I see from your application that you have recently completed some training. Could you tell me about this?	Give a structured answer, being clear about the broad areas of your course, how it was assessed, and how well you did.
3 What do you think you are good at?	Give a full answer, i.e. 'I think I am good at . . .because . . .'. Provide examples to back up what you say.
4 Could you tell me more about the jobs you have done so far?	Tie in your experience with the job description to provide evidence that you will be able to cope.
5 What particular qualities have you got that suit you for the job?	Highlight two or three, and again, tie them into the qualities you have drawn out from the job description.
6 What has been your greatest achievement to date?	This can be anything in your working or personal life. Provide background information and present it as relevant to the job on offer.
7 In what practical ways would you encourage the individuality of a client?	You can prepare for this kind of question beforehand, basing your answer on information on the job description. E.g. 'I would do this by . . .'.
8 I see you have no experience of housing associations. Do you think this will be a problem?	Do not pretend that you have if you have not! But answer positively by counterposing the question; i.e. 'No I don't have this experience, but I do have experience of . . . Do you think this will be a problem?'
9 What experience of meetings do you have?	Again, you can prepare for this by examining the job description. If you have little experience in this area, show that you are aware of the skills required.
10 Are there any questions you would like to ask about the job?	Do have some questions prepared – and not just about pay and holidays!

Do not worry if you found these difficult – they are meant to be. With luck, the questions you are asked will be much more straightforward, but it is wise to be prepared.

3 After the interview

All may not be over yet. Even if you feel entirely happy with your interview and are sure you want the job, keep looking and applying for others, until you have an offer of a job in writing. You may end up with a choice.

If after a reasonable period of time you are still unsuccessful then there comes point when you have to ask yourself some questions

- Am I applying for the wrong jobs?
- Am I approaching the applications wrongly?
- Am I coming across badly in interviews?

You may need advice, or simply the perseverance and self-confidence to know that you need to match your skills, personal qualities and experience with the opportunities there are. There will always be other people applying for the job; put yourself in the employer's shoes, and see what they are looking for.

Good luck!

Reference Section

1 How to check alphabetical order

Finding things that have been filed or listed alphabetically can be easier said than done. Make sure you know the way a particular filing system works.

1 Are names filed in strict alphabetical order, or are people with the same family name and address filed (in order) together?

2 Check the spelling carefully; Giorgio or Georgiou?

3 Look at the order of the letters well into the name; Garrett or Garratt?

4 Check the first names or initials: Gibson, Alan L; Gibson A W; Gibson, Graham; Gibson, J T; Gibson, Dr Michael.

5 Where two people have the same names or initials, check the address, and file alphabetically by the address.

ACTIVITY

☐ **1** You have been asked to file the following patients' notes in the correct alphabetical order. Rewrite this list in the order in which you would file the notes.

Luke Gibbons, 28 Oakland Road
Thomas D C Georgiou, 52 Allison Road
Geraets, P, 51 Claremont Rd
Karam Gill, 43 Kilbride Ho, Peters Close
John Gordon, 94 Loraine Rd
Gray, Eileen, 2a Hoyle Rd
Goldberg, B J, 8 Stapleford Rd
Alison Gibbs, 61 Newton Way
Geraldine Geraghty, 50d Fox Close
Nicholas M Georgiou, 52 Allison Rd
Gordon, J H, 33 Kings Ave
Geraghty, Michael, 13 Briscoe Rd
S Gupta, 293 Church Way
Ronald Gibbs, 61 Newton Way
Georgiou, Nicos, 7 Crossfield St
Rev J Geraerts, 193 Westfield Lane

Michael Geraghty, 27 Chaucer Ho, Acre St
Mrs K Gill, 6a North Park Rd
Jacqueline Gordon, 10 Elm Close
Margaret Gillingham 96a Byegrove St
Mrs E Grey, 2a, Hoyle Rd
Alexis J Georgiou, 52 Allison Rd
Grove, C T, 16 Du Cann Court, Burntwood Drive
Dr H Gordon, 32 Topsham Rd

2 You have been asked to return the following patients' notes to the correct position:

- Katerina Georgiou, 52 Allison Road
- Jonathan Gordon, 10 Elm Close
- Kevin Geraghty, 3 Latimer Rd.

3 'Can you get Mrs Grey's notes for me, please?'
Write down the questions you would need to ask to be sure to return with the correct notes.

2 How to punctuate

This section gives a outline of the basic rules of essential punctuation: full stops; capital letters; commas and apostrophes. If you need a fuller guide or further practice, there are plenty of books to refer to. The reference section of *Study Skills* by Kate Williams (Macmillan Professional Masters 1989) may be helpful to you.

Full stop

A full stop is used at the end of a sentence. This is the most important piece of punctuation because it divides writing into sentences, units that make sense.

ACTIVITY

☐ Punctuate the following passage:

People's expectations of what health care can offer have risen since the NHS was established in the past people took poor health or debilitating conditions for granted today people expect to be healthy and go to the doctor when they are not the very success of the NHS in improving the nation's health is causing it problems today higher expectations of health have led to increased demands on the health services conditions and diseases are treated now for which no treatment and often no diagnosis was possible in the past how to pay for the NHS and who should pay is the subject of on-going debate

Turn to pp 4–5 and compare your punctuation with the original.

Capital letters

Capital letters are used
1 to start sentences;
2 for names of individual people, places, days, months, organisations

(and acronyms of these organisations), products etc.: David Williams, Dr Harry Gordon, Lancashire, Nigeria, Wednesday, November, the Royal College of Nursing (acronym RCN), Pitmans, Savlon;

3   for the titles of books, films, programmes: *A Practical Approach to Caring, Blue Peter,* the *Activities of Daily Living.*

Check your handwriting to make sure that your capitals *look* different to your lower case letters. They should be taller and are often differently formed.

Commas

Commas must never be used as an alternative to full stops. They have several uses:

1   to mark off items in a list;
     Practitioners, planners, policy-makers and the government are in agreement . . . ' (*see* p 25).

2   To mark off a phrase which is not absolutely essential to the sentence.
     A single comma is used when the non-essential word or phrase comes first:
     'In addition, Gladys goes to the Occupational Therapy homemaking unit two mornings a week . . . ' (*see* p 57).
     A pair of commas is used when the non-essential word or phrase comes in the middle of the sentence:
     'He only just passed his 'A' levels, however, as he became very nervous and anxious at this time.' (*see* p 48).

3   To mark off direct speech from what comes before or after it.
     'She says, 'Oh no, thank you, but I had a lovely breakfast', when she offers to cook for Mrs Taylor . . . ' (*see* p 66).

4   To mark off phrases beginning with words such as when, after, unless, although, whey they come at the beginning or middle of a sentence.
     'As they get older, how will Andrew manage?' (*See* p 42).

ACTIVITY

☐   Punctuate the following passage:

In herself mrs taylor is a fine looking dignified old lady now a little frail clearly she and her husband enjoyed good things solid furniture find china books and music they were happy together and she finds she is missing him more as she gets older she is beginning to dread the future

Check it with the paragraph on p 66. See if you can correct all the punctuation and explain why each comma is used.

Apostrophes

Apostrophes have two uses only.

1   To mark missing letters.

He doesn't know   = He does not know
They'll come   = They will come
It's raining   = It is raining
I could've done it   = I could have done it

2   To show belonging.

(*a*) where something belongs to one person or thing, use **'s;**

- the client's view
- What is the ward's routine?

(*b*) where something belongs to more than one, add an apostrophe to the plural or 's to the plural form of the word:

- the students' study day
- the children's mother

Notice the difference between 'the students' study day (i.e. all the students have a study day) and 'the student's study day' (i.e. only one student has a study day).

Do not scatter apostrophes around wherever you see an 's'. The rules for using apostrophes are straightforward.

Further practice

The best way to learn to punctuate well is to look closely at what you read. Look back at, say, one paragraph and try and work out why each piece of punctuation has been used. You will soon find yourself spotting errors.

If you want further practice, tape yourself reading a paragraph from a book or article at a normal speed, then play it back, stopping to allow yourself time to write it down. Then compare your version with the original.

3 How to take messages

When you take a message, whether it is a phone message or from someone in person, you must record the following five points
- who the message is **to**;
- who it is **from**;
- **date** and **time** the message or call was received;
- the **subject** if not the actual **message**; and
- **who** took the message – i.e. your name.

You may take messages on scrappy bits of paper, or use a printed pad. Either way, these points must be covered in your message taking.
1   Identify these five points in the printed message pads below.
2   Copy out these message pads, and use them when you take messages.

To. . . . .
Date. . . . .

WHILE YOU WERE OUT
M . . . .
of . . . .
Phone No. . . . .

Telephoned		Please call	
Called to see you		Will call again	
Wants to see you		Urgent	

MESSAGE

. . . .
. . . .
. . . .
. . . .
. . . .

Operator . . . .

TELEPHONE MESSAGE

Time :

Date :

Returning
your call
☐

Will call
again
☐

Please
call back
☐

URGENT
☐

From :

Telephone No :

R
Ryman

4 How to write a memo

A memo is for internal correspondence, i.e. within your organisation. The content of a memo may be a short informal note, or longer – if the person worked in a different organisation, you might have written a longish letter.

The layout of a memo is designed to help you as a writer, and your reader, to put across your message as clearly and simply as possible. Most organisations have ready printed memo forms, which remind you to include this basic information. In any memo remember to show

- who it is **to**;
- who it is **from**;
- the **date**; and
- the **subject**.

Then write what you have to say, using short paragraphs, and initial and date your memo by hand at the end, whether the rest is handwritten or typed.

There may be other points to note in your organisation. Some memos will include

- **Copies to** (cc), showing who else receives the memo;
- **My reference**;
- **Your reference** to help the filing system of the people who write and receive the memo; and particular conventions, like initialling or ticking a memo once it has been read.

When you write a memo, keep it simple; just use the essential headings, as in the example below.

Memo

To   Linen Services Manager

From   Sister Josie Barnard, Ward Manager
Cherry Ward

Date   11 December 19--

Subject   <u>Supply of Linen to Cherry Ward</u>

For the past week the supply of sheets to the ward has been inadequate, and nursing time has been taken up daily with requesting, and on one occasion collecting, additional sheets.

Please ensure that you send the agreed number of sheets to the ward by 10.00am, as we cannot manage with fewer.

JB.

5 How to set out letters

A formal letter

Remember, a formal letter should:
- begin 'Dear Sir'
- end 'Yours faithfully'.

'Formal' means that you have not met; you do not know the name of the person you are writing to; and the business is formal.

A less formal letter

A less formal letter should:
- begin 'Dear Ms (or Mr, Mrs, Miss) Clarke; and
- end 'Your sincerely'.

Less formal means you know who you are writing to; you *may* have met; and want to adopt a more personal tone. You may come across the opening. 'Dear Angela Clarke' where people correspond on a professional and equal basis. Do not use it yourself.

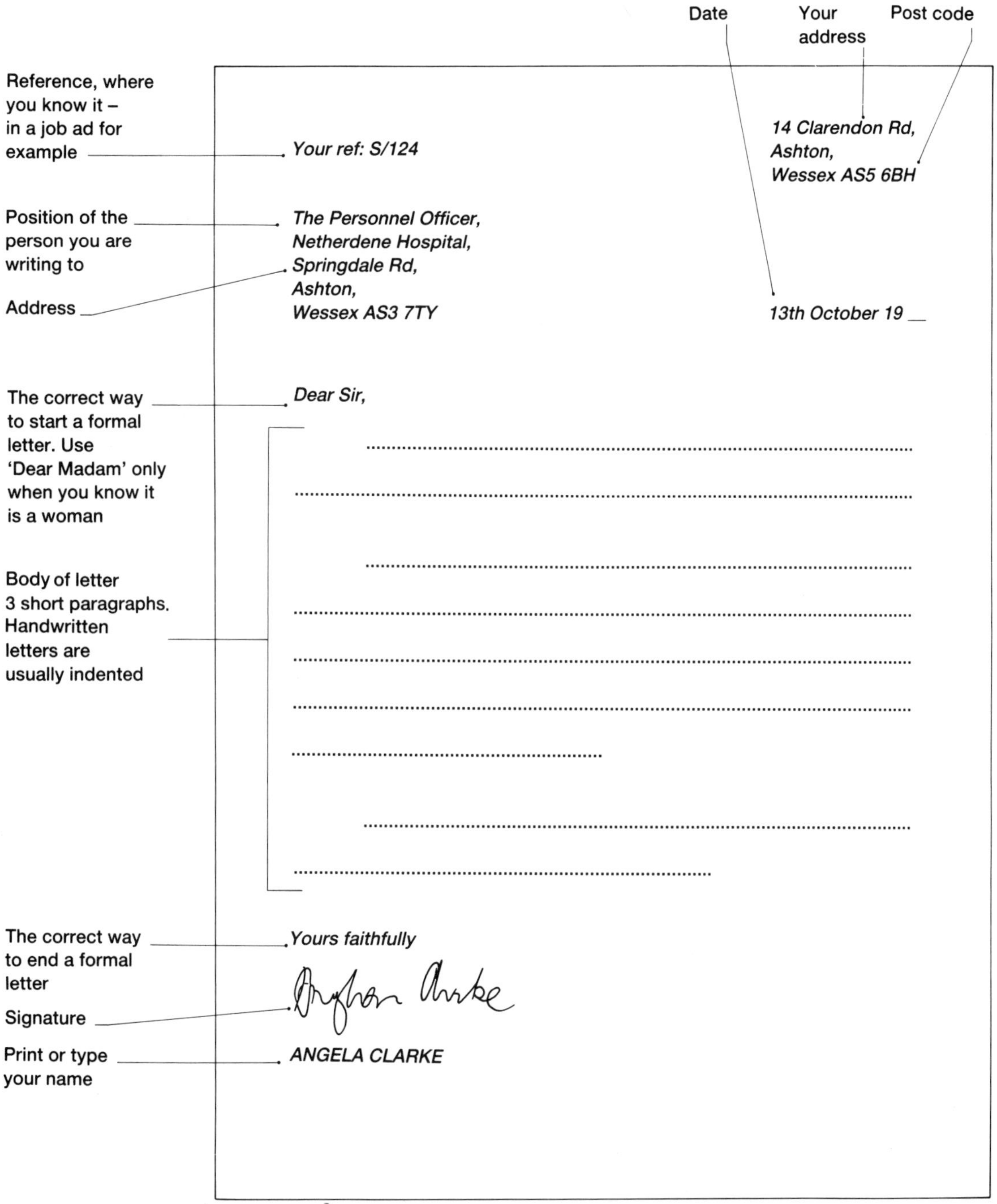

Date　　　Your　　　Post code
address

Reference, where
you know it –
in a job ad for
example ——————— ·Your ref: S/124

14 Clarendon Rd,
Ashton,
Wessex AS5 6BH

Position of the ——————— ·The Personnel Officer,
person you are　　　　　　　Netherdene Hospital,
writing to　　　　　　　　·Springdale Rd,
　　　　　　　　　　　　　Ashton,
Address ———————　　　Wessex AS3 7TY　　　　13th October 19 __

The correct way ——————— ·Dear Sir,
to start a formal
letter. Use
'Dear Madam' only
when you know it
is a woman

Body of letter
3 short paragraphs.
Handwritten
letters are
usually indented

The correct way ——————— ·Yours faithfully
to end a formal
letter

Signature ———————

Print or type ——————— ·ANGELA CLARKE
your name

A formal letter

Address of writer.
Most organisations
have already-printed
letter headings

An organisation needs
to file letters, so uses
a reference, usually the
initials of the writer.
Quote this of you write
back

Our ref: S/124/MH

Personnel Office
Netherdene Hospital
Springdale Road
Ashton
Wessex AS3 7TY

Name and address of
person written to

Ms A Clarke
14 Clarendon Rd
Ashton
Wessex AS5 6HB

29th October 19_ _

Is Angela Clarke
Mrs or Miss? So use Ms

Dear Ms Clarke

....

....

Most organisations
use fully blocked
layout (nothing indented)
and open punctuation
(only the text of the
letter is punctuated)

....

....

....

....

....

....

....

The correct way to end
a less formal letter

Yours sincerely

Signature

Typed name and position

Margaret Hennesey
Personnel Officer

A less formal letter

6 How to draw up a questionnaire

First be clear about **what** you want to find out; **how** you are going to find it out; and consider how you are going to present it. You may want to distribute your questionnaire for people to fill in on their own or decide to use it as the basis for interviews you carry out yourself. Consider the advantages and disadvantages of each.

What sort of questions?

Look at the style of the following questions which could be used to collect information on people's smoking habits in Assignment 7.

1 Do you smoke cigarettes?   *Yes/No*
   (If 'No' ask Question 2. If 'Yes', move on to Question 4)
2 Have you ever smoked cigarettes?   *Yes/No*
   (If *'Yes'* ask Question 3)
3 How long ago did you give up smoking?
   • within the last year
   • 1–5 years ago
   • over 5 years ago
4 What are your views on smoking?

Questions 1 and 2 are examples of **closed** questions. The interviewee has to choose from fixed answers, in this case 'Yes' or 'No'.
Question 3 is also closed, a follow-up question you would only ask people replying 'No' to Question 1 and 'Yes' to Question 2.
Question 4 is an **open** question which is useful if you are interested in people's attitudes. You will often find out interesting and unexpected information in response to open-ended questions but it is more difficult to quantify these answers and to know how to present the information.

Most questions in a questionnaire should be **closed**. They are easy to sort and can be presented clearly as percentages, pie charts or bar charts.

Use the index to find examples of these in the book.

Your style of question is also important in communicating with clients (*see* Assignment 31 Coming into hospital).

Wording

The wording of question is important. When you have decided on the questions you want to ask try them on a few friends. Check whether:

- they understood the questions;
- they produced the sorts of answers you expected; and
- there were too many, or too few questions.

Then decide

- Your sample – how many people you want to complete the questionnaire. You can get quite a large sample if you agree on a single questionnaire for the whole group – 15 people each interviewing 10 people gives you a sample of 150.
- who to interview: junior/senior staff, people in the street, clients?
- whether you want a balance of ages, sex, lifestyles. How will you achieve this?
- a deadline for completing the questionnaires.

Using a tape recorder

If you decide to use a tape recorder, practise with it first. Set the counter at 0 for the interview and when you play it back, stop it when you come to an interesting bit, note the number on the counter. This will save you time later.

Presentation

When you have completed the questionnaires and compiled your results, you need to think about the most effective way of presenting them. Bar charts and pie charts might show some results at a glance – for example, whether people overwhelmingly support a ban on smoking in public places – or not!

7 How to write a report

1 A verbal report

'Yes, I have just checked the linen store. There are plenty of pillow cases but not many sheets. I don't think there are enough sheets for the morning. I think we should phone through to Supplies and ask them to send some more over before lunch.'

This is a good investigative report. It is short and useful and gives clear, well structured information.

2 A written investigative report

A formal investigative report supports the logical structure of the verbal report above with conventions.

Introduction
1 Subject heading or title
2 Terms of reference   : what you have been asked to find out
(whether there is enough bed linen)
3 Procedure   : how you found out
(a personal check)

Body
4 Findings   : what you found out
(plenty of pillow cases but not many sheets)

Conclusion
5 Conclusion   : your conclusions or diagnosis
(not enough sheets for the morning)
6 Recommendations   : what you think should be done
(phone Supplies and ask for more sheets).

In an informal, short report like this you would not use these headings but I have used them in this example to show how the structure of a formal report helps all report writing.

In an informal report write your report in three paragraphs using the headings 'Introduction', 'Body' (or 'findings'), and 'Conclusion', and structure your information in the report in the same way as the formal report.

3 A report of an event

This is a more usual type of report, where you are asked to give an account of an event, incident or accident. Shown opposite is an **accident report form.** Try completing it, changing details as appropriate, to give an account of any incident, however minor, that occurs during your time in training.

Form no 36758   **DESEWORTH HEALTH AUTHORITY**

Hospital ....
Ward ....

Part 1 *To be completed by nursing staff*
Details of injured person
Name in full ....
Address ....
....
Date of birth ....

Place of accident ....
Date and time of accident ....
If any equipment or apparatus is involved this should be retained for inspection

Description of accident and cause if known

Action taken

Staff on duty at the time 1
                           2
                           3
                           4
Name and signature of person making report
....
Countersigned (Senior duty nurse)
....

For staff only: Signature of injured person ....

Part 2 *To be completed by medical officer*
Nature and extent of injuries ....
Treatment ordered ....
For staff only: Whether incapacitated for duty ....
....
                Probable duration of absence
....
Signed ....   Date ....

8 How to give a talk or presentation

When you start thinking about giving a talk or presentation, think first about your listeners:
- Who are they?
- What do they know about your topic?
- What might they want to learn?
- What would cause them to switch off?

Once you have thought about your audience and what they might want from your talk, you can then work out how to
- make your talk interesting;
- keep them awake and involved; and
- pitch your talk right, i.e. not too complicated, but not too simple. It is hard to be too simple when you are talking about something you know about.

Then structure your talk so it is easy to follow. Plan three parts.
1   **In your introduction.** Look at different members of your audience in the eye, take a deep breath, smile and start slowly.
    (a) Get the attention of your audience; and
    (b) outline the main areas of your talk;
2   **In your body of your talk**
    (a) plan which points you will put across in words only
    (b) which points or explanations are more effective/memorable/ stimulating when you combine our comments with another device:
- flipchart
- asking the audience to do a specific (short) task
- questions and feedback
- demonstration/display
- charts/diagrams/pictures/maps
- handouts (but be sure how you are going to use them or your audience will be reading instead of listening to you)
- tape/slides/video or film clip.
3   **In your conclusion.** Review your main points – focus on the essentials

you want them to remember. How to do this?
- an example or anecdote that ties it all together?
- a summary?
- a look ahead?

Never introduce new points in your conclusion.

Throughout your presentation:
- look at your audience.
- Be prepared to repeat, go more slowly, add details, in response to how you feel they are reacting.
- Get your timing right. You don't want to rush through because you took too long to get going nor spin it out because you haven't got enough to say.
- Give examples, repeat points, make the point in several ways. This gives your listeners time for the important points to sink in.
- If there is something funny, that's fine. Shared humour often helps – but don't crack jokes. They tend to fall flat.

Answers

Assignment 6: As others see us
Task 4 (*b*)

(*Answers*)
1 17%
2 79%
3 15%
4 True
5 44%
6   3%
7 78%
8   3%
9 True
10 5–7%
11 False
12 150
13 True
14 True
15 37%
16 True
17   8%
18 True
19 False
20 81

Assignment 14: Danger at home
Task 4: Do you know what to do?
(*Answers to First Aid Quiz*)
1 (*c*)
2 (*b*)
3 (*a*)
4 (*d*)
5 (*b*)
6 (*b*)
7 (*d*)
8 (*c*)
9 (*c*)
10 (*d*)

Assignment 18: Food hygiene
Task 5: What to do and say
(*a*) (ii)
(*b*) (iii)
(*c*) (i)
(*d*) (ii)
(*e*) (i)
(*f*) (iii)
(*g*) (iii)

NVQ Index

Health Care Support Worker

National Vocational Qualifications (NVQs) are designed to accredit demonstrated competence in the workplace. The activities in this book complement and promote a wide range of NVQ qualifications in care and health care at Levels 1, 2 and 3. The Care Sector Consortium is currently devising the National Occupational Standards for the full range of occupations in the care sector and the first to be published in a final form are those for Health Care Support Workers.

This NVQ index of the National Occupational Standards for Health Care Support Workers illustrates how this book can be used to support work towards NVQs in a specific occupational area, as details of these become available.

The diagram overleaf shows how the NVQ units make up the **key roles** of the Health Care Support Worker.

Each NVQ **unit** comprises a number of **elements**, for each of which the candidate must meet specific **performance criteria**. These offer precise guidance as to the tasks the candidate should be able to carry out and the manner in which caring tasks are undertaken. The **evidence specification** gives guidance as to how competence, in terms of both **performance** and **knowledge**, should be assessed.

SUPPORT CLIENTS AND PROFESSIONALS IN THE DELIVERY OF CARE

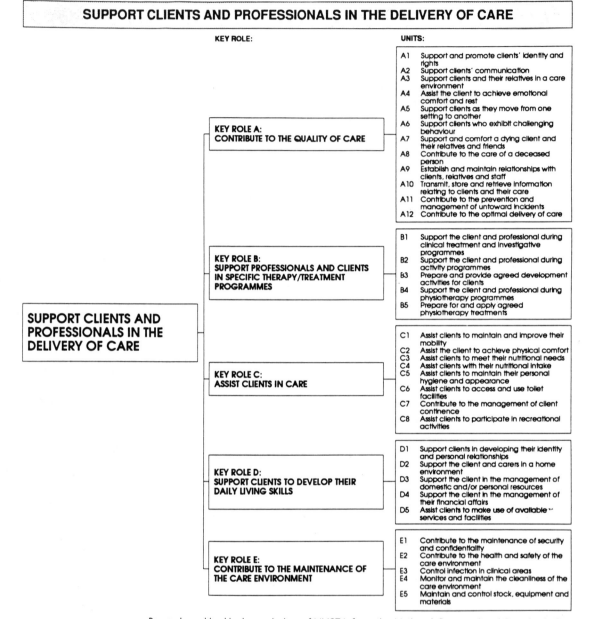

KEY ROLE:

UNITS:

SUPPORT CLIENTS AND PROFESSIONALS IN THE DELIVERY OF CARE

KEY ROLE A:
CONTRIBUTE TO THE QUALITY OF CARE

A1	Support and promote clients' identity and rights
A2	Support clients' communication
A3	Support clients and their relatives in a care environment
A4	Assist the client to achieve emotional comfort and rest
A5	Support clients as they move from one setting to another
A6	Support clients who exhibit challenging behaviour
A7	Support and comfort a dying client and their relatives and friends
A8	Contribute to the care of a deceased person
A9	Establish and maintain relationships with clients, relatives and staff
A10	Transmit, store and retrieve information relating to clients and their care
A11	Contribute to the prevention and management of untoward incidents
A12	Contribute to the optimal delivery of care

KEY ROLE B:
SUPPORT PROFESSIONALS AND CLIENTS IN SPECIFIC THERAPY/TREATMENT PROGRAMMES

B1	Support the client and professional during clinical treatment and investigative programmes
B2	Support the client and professional during activity programmes
B3	Prepare and provide agreed development activities for clients
B4	Support the client and professional during physiotherapy programmes
B5	Prepare for and apply agreed physiotherapy treatments

KEY ROLE C:
ASSIST CLIENTS IN CARE

C1	Assist clients to maintain and improve their mobility
C2	Assist the client to achieve physical comfort
C3	Assist clients to meet their nutritional needs
C4	Assist clients with their nutritional intake
C5	Assist clients to maintain their personal hygiene and appearance
C6	Assist clients to access and use toilet facilities
C7	Contribute to the management of client continence
C8	Assist clients to participate in recreational activities

KEY ROLE D:
SUPPORT CLIENTS TO DEVELOP THEIR DAILY LIVING SKILLS

D1	Support clients in developing their identity and personal relationships
D2	Support the client and carers in a home environment
D3	Support the client in the management of domestic and/or personal resources
D4	Support the client in the management of their financial affairs
D5	Assist clients to make use of available services and facilities

KEY ROLE E:
CONTRIBUTE TO THE MAINTENANCE OF THE CARE ENVIRONMENT

E1	Contribute to the maintenance of security and confidentiality
E2	Contribute to the health and safety of the care environment
E3	Control infection in clinical areas
E4	Monitor and maintain the cleanliness of the care environment
E5	Maintain and control stock, equipment and materials

Reproduced by kind permission of NHSTA from the National Occupational Standards Care Sector Consortium Health Care Support Worker Project.

In the index which follows, NVQ units are referenced by number to (assignments (A), case studies (CS), reference section (Ref) and specific pages (p).

* These units are not currently allocated to an NVQ.

Index